ABOUT THE AUTHOR

Kim-Mai Cutler is a third-generation Bay Area resident and an operating partner at Initialized Capital, an early-stage venture firm that has invested in companies like Cruise, Flexport, Plangrid, Coinbase and Patreon. Before that, she was a technology and financial journalist covering early-stage and growth startups for publications like TechCrunch, Bloomberg and The Wall Street Journal. She serves on San Francisco's Local Homeless Coordinating Board, which oversees federal funding for homeless programs across the city.

ABOUT THE ILLUSTRATOR

Kelsey Westphal (also known as Krusty Wheatfield) was born in Ojai, California, where she climbed lots of trees and read books all day. At UC Berkeley she studied English and French, got sidetracked by her friends in the art department and started making zines and drawing comics. After working as a bookbinder, poet's assistant, dogsitter, babysitter, illustrator, bartender, and writing tutor in the Bay Area, she was awarded an artist's residency in St. Louis, Senegal, where she wrote a 70-page comic amidst the 2015 Ebola outbreak, and then fled to the international comics hub of Europe, Angoulême, France, where she received a Research Masters in Text/Image Relations (or Comics) at the École Européenne Supérieure de l'Image. Her favorite memory of that time was spending a week in Brussels with the SuperStructure collective constructing an obstacle course in a squat for a zine release party. She wrote two really long theses that galvanized her belief in the power of comics to communicate important, nuanced ideas in an accessible and inventive way. Now back in Oakland, she organizes events at a local venue and creates nonfiction and political cartoons. When she has free time she tries to make music and perform rites of worship to her roommate's chihuahua, Mushroom. Her dream is to be a full time adventure cartoonist and write the Moby Dick of cartoon journalism.

HOW BURROWING OWLS LEAD TO VOMITING ANARCHISTS

OR

SAN FRANCISCO'S HOUSING CRISIS EXPLAINED

ISBN 978-0-692-88022-7

Library of Congress Control Number 2017944134

Adapted from "How Burrowing Owls Lead To Vomiting Anarchists (Or SF's Housing Crisis Explained)" published on TechCrunch, April 14, 2014, by Kim-Mai Cutler. https://techcrunch.com/2014/04/14/sf-housing/

Illustrations and layout by Kelsey Westphal
www.krustywheatfield.com

Edited by Diego Aguilar-Canabal and Milo Trauss
Additional editing by Laura Fingal-Surma
Additional layout by Rashel Cordova

Printed and bound in the United States of America
Second Edition September 2017

Published by Bay Area Metropolitan Observer and YIMBY Action
www.sfbamo.com
www.yimbyaction.org

FOREWORD

This is a graphic novel adaptation of a 13,000-word story that I wrote three years ago in 2014. I never expected when I pressed publish that night in April 2014, that this very long blog post on TechCrunch would become part of a Bay Area movement to build more housing in California.

Since then, countless groups from YIMBY Action to East Bay Forward to Palo Alto Forward have cropped up to pressure local leaders to build more units to address a profound jobs-housing imbalance in the region. Between 2011 and 2015, the Bay Area added a half-million jobs but only 65,000 housing units, or one unit of housing for every eight jobs.[1] Housing has also emerged as the top issue for the California state legislature, with 130 bills currently floating through the Senate and Assembly.[2]

When YIMBY Action asked me if they could bring on Kelsey Westphal to do a comic book version of the original piece, I was pretty excited to expose a lot of very arcane concepts around land-use and zoning to a broader audience and a younger generation.

This book is an entry point for anyone looking to learn about the history of housing in the Bay Area, as the original essay was for so many people now working to change things. Of course, three years later there are things that have shifted or that I feel I under-emphasized in the original piece. I have included an afterword that addresses a few structural issues that deserve wider attention and understanding, on top of all of the local pressures I explained in the original piece.

The afterword covers critical issues such as the regressive nature of our federal housing subsidies in America and the distortions to the California housing market brought on by Proposition 13. There is much to be said about the role of capital, tech companies and the bizarre incentives at work in the Bay Area housing market.

Overall, California's system allows land and property to soak up a disproportionate share of economic growth, which channels capital toward less productive and less innovative uses and de-stabilizes low-income residents who don't have the resources or wages to keep up with rising rents. Fixing it will require changes to governance that enhance regional planning and significant tax reform at the state and municipal levels.

If the YIMBY message of building more housing is sometimes criticized for being too simplistic, that's because building more housing is the simplest—still incredibly difficult—option to pursue.

— Kim-Mai Cutler, May 2017

THE SANTA CLARA VALLEY WAS SOME OF THE MOST VALUABLE AGRICULTURAL LAND IN THE WORLD

BUT

THIS WAS SIMPLY THE RESULT OF :

IT WAS PAVED OVER TO CREATE TODAY'S SILICON VALLEY.

BAD PLANNING

&

LAYERS OF LEADERSHIP FAILURE

 ≠

NOBODY THINKS FARMS LITERALLY NEEDED TO BE DESTROYED TO CREATE THE TECHNOLOGY INDUSTRY'S SUCCESS.

TODAY, THE TECH INDUSTRY IS APPARENTLY ON TRACK TO DESTROY ONE OF THE WORLD'S CULTURAL TREASURES.

SAN FRANCISCO

BY PUSHING OUT ALL THE DIVERSE PEOPLE WHO HAVE HELPED CREATE IT

AT LEAST THAT'S THE STORY YOU'VE BEEN READING IN HUNDREDS OF ARTICLES LATELY

1

IT DOESN'T HAVE TO BE THIS WAY.

BUT EVERYONE IN THE BAY AREA NEEDS TO ACCEPT RESPONSIBILITY FOR MAKING CHANGES WHERE THEY LIVE SO THAT EVERYONE WHO WANTS TO BE HERE, **CAN.**

THE ALTERNATIVE,

INACTION & SELF-ABSORPTION

AMEX ONLY

CCTV CCTV

KEEP OUT!

NO TRESPASS

SPARE A DOLLAR?

VERY WELL COULD CREATE THE CYNICAL ELITE PARADISE & MIDDLE CLASS DYSTOPIA THAT MANY FEAR.

KIM-MAI CUTLER
(AUTHOR OF THIS ARTICLE)

I'VE SPENT TIME LOOKING INTO THE CITY'S HISTORICAL

HOUSING & DEVELOPMENT POLICIES

WITH PROTESTS ESCALATING AGAIN,

STOP! TECH!

NO!

NO VACANCY

I'M PRETTY TIRED OF SEEING THE CITY'S YOUNG & DISENFRANCHISED FIGHT EACH OTHER AMID AN EXTREME HOUSING SHORTAGE CREATED BY 30 to 40 YEARS OF

NIMBY-ISM
NOT IN MY BACK YARD

FROM THE OLD WEALTH OF THE CITY

AND

DOWN FROM THE PENINSULA SUBURBS

HERE IS A VERY LONG EXPLAINER.

BUT IF YOU'RE WONDERING WHY PEOPLE ARE PROTESTING YOU

THIS IS A COMPLEX PROBLEM

AND I'M NOT GOING TO DISTILL IT INTO

YOUNG, RICH TECH DOUCHEBAGS

VS

HELPLESS OLD LADIES FACING EVICTION

THERE ARE MANY OTHER PLACES WHERE YOU CAN READ THAT STORY.

IT DOES US ALL

NO JUSTICE

FIRST OFF,

UNDERSTAND THE MATH OF THE REGION.

TOTAL HOUSING UNITS: 376,942

65% RENTAL UNITS

35% HOMEOWNERSHIP RATE

172,000 OF THESE ARE RENT-CONTROLLED

THAT'S ABOUT 75% OF THE CITY'S RENTAL STOCK

WHICH LEAVES US WITH 16.25% OF SF's HOUSING STOCK AT MARKET-RATE

HOMEOWNERS HAVE A STRONG ECONOMIC INCENTIVE TO RESTRICT SUPPLY

BECAUSE IT SUPPORTS PRICE APPRECIATION OF THEIR OWN HOMES.

FOREVER MINE

IT'S UNDERSTANDABLE.

MANY OF THEM HAVE PUT THE BULK OF THEIR NET WORTH INTO THEIR HOMES & THEY DON'T WANNA LOSE THAT

NET $ WORTH

SO THEY ENGAGE IN NIMBYism

UNDER THE NAME OF PRESERVATIONISM OR ENVIRONMENTALISM,

TO BE CLEAR: NOT ALL HOMEOWNERS WANT MASSIVE APPRECIATION, BUT PROP. 13 LEAVES MANY INSULATED OR DESENSITIZED TO THE SHIFTING COSTS OF LAND & RENTS.

EVEN THOUGH DENYING INFILL
DEVELOPMENT **HERE** CREATES
PRESSURES FOR SPRAWL
ELSEWHERE.

THEY DO THIS THROUGH
HUNDREDS OF POLITICALLY
POWERFUL NEIGHBORHOOD GROUPS
LIKE THE TELEGRAPH HILL DWELLERS.

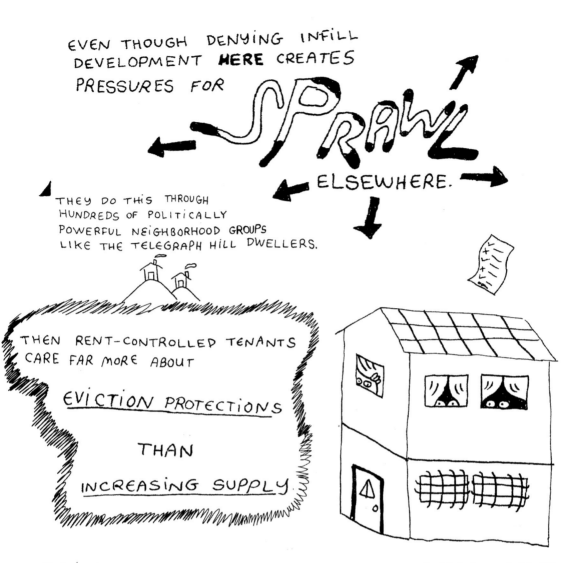

THEN RENT-CONTROLLED TENANTS
CARE FAR MORE ABOUT

EVICTION PROTECTIONS

THAN

INCREASING SUPPLY.

THAT'S BECAUSE THEIR MOST VULNERABLE CONSTITUENTS ARE PAYING RENTS

SO FAR BELOW

MARKET-RATE
THAT ONLY AN UNGODLY AMOUNT
OF CONSTRUCTION COULD POSSIBLY HELP THEM.

PLUS, THAT CONSTRUCTION WOULDN'T HAPPEN
FAST ENOUGH — ESPECIALLY FOR ELDERLY
TENANTS.

SO WE'RE LOOKING AT AS MUCH AS **80%** OF S.F. THAT ISN'T NATURALLY ORIENTED TO ADD TO HOUSING STOCK

OH, AND **TECH?** THE INDUSTRY IS ABOUT **11%** OF THE WORKFORCE.

THEN IF YOU LOOK AT CITIES DOWN ON THE PENINSULA & IN THE TRADITIONAL HEART OF SILICON VALLEY, **IT'S EVEN WORSE.**

THE GOOGLE BUS PROTESTERS SAID THAT

THE COMPANY SHOULD BUILD HOUSING ON ITS CAMPUS!

BUT THE MOUNTAIN VIEW CITY COUNCIL HAD EXPRESSLY FORBIDDEN GOOGLE FROM DOING JUST THAT.

THEY'VE ARGUED THAT IT'S TO
PROTECT THE CITY'S BURROWING
OWL POPULATION.

THE CITY COUNCIL EVEN CREATED
A FERAL CAT TASK FORCE TO
PROTECT THE OWLS.

IF YOU LOOK AT THE
JOB - TO - HOUSING RATIO
IN OTHER PENINSULA CITIES
LIKE PALO ALTO, ITS PRETTY
TERRIBLE

STRAY
CATS

SO THE WEALTHY VOTING CLASSES
OF THE PENINSULA ARE STRANGLING
THEMSELVES OUT OF HOUSING TOO.

THE MEDIAN RENT IN
MOUNTAIN VIEW IS

$**3,500**   compared to   **3,410***
IN SAN FRANCISCO.

*ZILLOW, 2017

CERTAIN CITIES LIKE MENLO PARK
ARE MORE COLLABORATIVE.

FACEBOOK PARTNERED WITH
DEVELOPERS TO BUILD A

1,500-UNIT COMPLEX

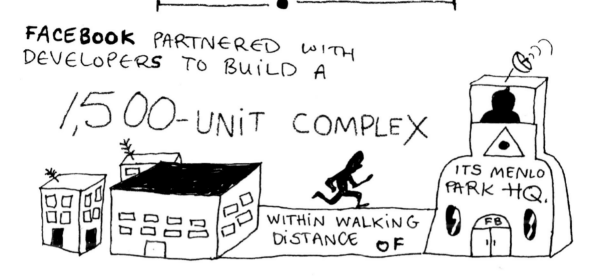

WITHIN WALKING
DISTANCE OF

ITS MENLO
PARK HQ.

BUT THATS **1500** UNITS FOR A COMPANY

WITH MORE THAN **17,048** EMPLOYEES.

SO → ONE CONTRIBUTOR TO THE TECH INDUSTRY'S
SPREAD INTO SAN FRANCISCO IS THAT THE
PENINSULA CITIES ARE MORE THAN HAPPY TO

VOTE FOR

JUST NOT

JOBS

HOMES

THIS IS A DEMOGRAPHIC SHIFT THAT IS MUCH LARGER THAN THE TECHNOLOGY INDUSTRY ITSELF— ALTHOUGH THERE ARE SOME TECH-SPECIFIC REASONS THAT HAVE FUELED A MIGRATION NORTH FROM THE HISTORIC HEART OF SILICON VALLEY OVER THE LAST 10 YEARS.

THIS IS WHAT URBANIST

CALLS "THE GREAT INVERSION"

A MAJOR SHIFT WHERE CITIES & SUBURBS HAVE TRADED PLACES OVER THE LAST 30 TO 40 YEARS.

AS PEOPLE MARRY LATER & EMPLOYMENT BECOMES MORE TEMPORAL, YOUNG ADULTS & AFFLUENT RETIREES ARE MOVING INTO THE URBAN CORE

WHILE IMMIGRANTS & THE LESS AFFLUENT ARE MOVING OUT.

SAN FRANCISCO'S POPULATION HIT A TROUGH AROUND 1980, AFTER STEADILY DECLINING SINCE THE 1950s AS THE CITY'S SOCIALLY CONSERVATIVE WHITE & IRISH-CATHOLIC POPULATION LEFT FOR THE SUBURBS.

INTO THE VACUUM OF RELATIVELY CHEAP RENTS CAME THE MISFITS, HIPPIES & IMMIGRANTS THAT FOMENTED SO MANY OF SAN FRANCISCO'S BEAUTIFULLY WEIRD CULTURAL & SEXUAL REVOLUTIONS

BUT THAT OUT-MIGRATION REVERSED AROUND 1980 & THE CITY'S POPULATION HAS BEEN STEADILY RISING

THIS IS A PHENOMENON THAT'S HAPPENING IN CITIES

ITS RAPACIOUS SPEED MAY EVEN BE

ACCELERATING →

WITNESS HYPER-GENTRIFICATION IN BROOKLYN & MANHATTAN,

OR THE "SHOREDITCH-IFICATION" OF LONDON

WHY?

PEOPLE ARE GETTING MARRIED LATER & LIVING LONGER

THE JOB MARKET HAS CHANGED AS WELL

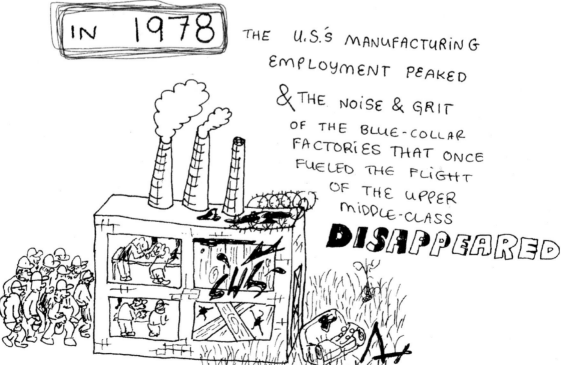

IN 1978 THE U.S.'s MANUFACTURING EMPLOYMENT PEAKED & THE NOISE & GRIT OF THE BLUE-COLLAR FACTORIES THAT ONCE FUELED THE FLIGHT OF THE UPPER MIDDLE-CLASS **DISAPPEARED**

THESE VACANT MANUFACTURING WAREHOUSES TURNED INTO THE LIVE-WORK LOFTS & SPACES THAT EMERGED IN THE '80s & 90s IN CITIES LIKE NEW YORK & SAN FRANCISCO.

THE CONCEPT OF LIFETIME EMPLOYMENT ALSO FADED.

TODAY, SAN FRANCISCO'S YOUNGER WORKERS DERIVE THEIR JOB SECURITY NOT FROM ANY SINGLE EMPLOYER BUT FROM A LARGE NETWORK OF WEAK TIES THAT LAST FROM ONE COMPANY TO THE NEXT.

THE DENSITY OF CITIES FAVORS THIS JOB-HOPPING BEHAVIOR MORE THAN SUBURBIA.

THERE ARE SOME TECH INDUSTRY-SPECIFIC REASONS TOO.

 REQUIRED TO FOUND A COMPANY & LAUNCH A MINIMUM VIABLE PRODUCT ARE MUCH LOWER THAN A DECADE AGO.

START-UPS ALSO NEED FEWER PEOPLE,

SO ITS EASIER FOR LOTS OF SMALL COMPANIES TO FIND POCKETS OF COMMERCIAL REAL ESTATE IN THE CITY FOR NEW OFFICES.

ITS ALSO EASY FOR VC's TO FUND AN ORDER OF MAGNITUDE MORE EXPERIMENTS, EVEN IF THE SAME PROPORTION OF THEM FAILS.

IN THE 1970's "SILICON VALLEY" LITERALLY MEANT MAKING SEMI-CONDUCTORS IN LARGE FABS THAT REQUIRED EXPENSIVE EQUIPMENT & CLEAN ROOMS

BUT THE BIG WAVE OF THE LAST DECADE HAS BEEN SOCIAL NETWORKING

AND EVERY NOTABLE PRODUCT OF THIS WAVE HAS BEEN SEEDED THROUGH "CRITICAL MASS" IN THE ANALOG WORLD.

FACEBOOK HAD UNIVERSITY CAMPUSES

SNAPCHAT HAD SO-CAL HIGH SCHOOLS

FOURSQUARE HAD LOWER MANHATTAN

TWITTER HAD SAN FRANCISCO

THESE PRODUCTS FAVOR **SOCIAL DENSITY**

AN EVEN NEWER GENERATION OF STARTUPS ADDRESSES DISTINCTLY URBAN QUESTIONS.

— AIRBNB EXISTS BECAUSE IN 2007, SF DIDN'T HAVE ENOUGH HOTEL CAPACITY TO HOUSE VISITORS IN TOWN FOR AN INDUSTRIAL DESIGN CONFERENCE.

UBER EXISTS BECAUSE THE CITY'S TAXI MARKET WAS UNDERSUPPLIED W/ DRIVERS

WHILE TECH IS FUELING THE CITY'S CURRENT BOOM, & HAS HELPED CUT SF'S UNEMPLOYMENT RATE IN HALF (?) SINCE 2010, THIS GENTRIFICATION WAVE HAS BEEN GOING ON FOR DECADES LONGER THAN THE WORD DOT-COM HAS EXISTED.

THEY HAVE TO DO THIS IN THE FACE OF GLOBAL ECONOMIC CHANGES THAT ARE DIVIDING OUR WORKERS INTO

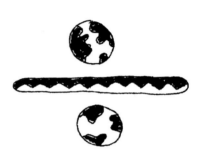

HIGHLY-SKILLED KNOWLEDGE WORKERS WHO ARE DISPROPORTIONATELY BENEFITTING FROM GROWTH

SERVICE WORKERS THAT ARE NOT SEEING THEIR WAGES RISE AT ALL.

3. OK, LET'S BUILD MORE HOUSING!

WOULDN'T THAT BE SIMPLE?

ITS NOT THAT EASY.

WHILE THE REAL ESTATE MARKET IS HOT, DEVELOPERS ARE CURRENTLY TALKING ABOUT BUILDING

TO GO BEYOND THAT, YOU HAVE TO BUILD POLITICAL WILL.

× × × ✊ ◆ ✊ × × ×

YOU HAVE TO WIN HEARTS & MINDS

YOU HAVE TO MAKE SURE THAT PEOPLE DON'T GET PUSHED OUT OR LEFT BEHIND.

THE CITY'S HEIGHT LIMITS, ITS RENT CONTROL, & ITS **FORMIDABLE**

PERMITTING PROCESS

ARE ALL PRODUCTS OF

TENANT, ENVIRONMENTAL & PRESERVATIONIST

MOVEMENTS OVER DECADES.

EVEN BACK IN 1967, THOUSANDS OF LATINO
RESIDENTS IN THE MISSION — *THE HEART OF THE
GENTRIFICATION BATTLE TODAY* — ORGANIZED

& CONVINCED SF'S BOARD OF SUPERVISORS
TO VOTE DOWN AN URBAN RENEWAL
PROGRAM IN THE NEIGHBORHOOD.

●

THEY SAW WHAT HAD HAPPENED TO THE
FILLMORE
ONCE THE

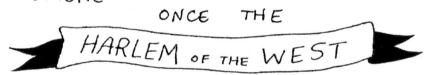

HARLEM OF THE WEST

WHEN THE CITY'S RE-DEVELOPMENT AGENCY
RAZED IT, DISPLACING TENS OF THOUSANDS
OF BLACK RESIDENTS & THE BUSINESSES
THEY HAD CREATED AFTER WWII.

TO THIS DAY THERE'S DISTRUST & FEAR THAT THE SAME THING WILL HAPPEN AGAIN

ESPECIALLY IF ITS CARRIED OUT BY PRIVATE DEVELOPERS.

ADVOCACY GROUP

CAUSA JUSTA
UNITY POWER · LA UNION
JUST CAUSE

HAS BEEN DOCUMENTING THIS DISPLACEMENT THROUGH CENSUS DATA

THEY NOTED THAT IN THE MISSION

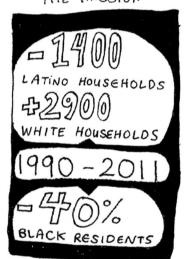

-1400 LATINO HOUSEHOLDS
+2900 WHITE HOUSEHOLDS
1990 - 2011
-40% BLACK RESIDENTS

DURING THE FIRST TECH BOOM, THERE WAS A

MISSION ANTI-DISPLACEMENT COALITION

WHICH PUSHED FOR A MORATORIUM ON NEW MARKET-RATE HOUSING & LIVE-WORK LOFTS IN THE NEIGHBORHOOD.

THROUGHOUT THE YEARS, THESE MOVEMENTS
HAVE FOUND ALLIANCES W/OTHER
NEIGHBORHOOD ORGANIZATIONS,
PRESERVATIONIST & ENVIRONMENTAL INTERESTS.

THERE WERE STRUGGLES IN THE 1950s & 60s
TO STOP FREEWAYS FROM CUTTING THROUGH
THE PANHANDLE & GOLDEN GATE PARK.

THIS GAVE RISE TO ANOTHER SLOW-GROWTH
POLITICAL MOVEMENT IN THE 1970s
TO PUSH BACK ON

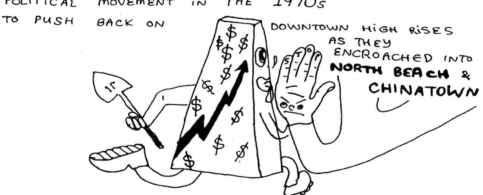

DOWNTOWN HIGH RISES
AS THEY
ENCROACHED INTO
**NORTH BEACH &
CHINATOWN**

IN 1986, THE CITY PASSED A RESOLUTION
TO CONTROL THE AMOUNT OF NEW COMMERCIAL
REAL ESTATE THAT COULD BE BUILT IN ANY
SINGLE YEAR.

TO THIS DAY

1972's TRANSAMERICA PYRAMID
REMAINS SAN FRANCISCO'S TALLEST BUILDING.

1,070 FT

FT

IT'S ONLY IN 2017
THAT THE TALLER
1,070 FT TOWER
ANCHORED BY
SALESFORCE
WILL OPEN

→ ONE SIDE EFFECT IS THAT →

 SAN FRANCISCO HAS ADDED AN AVERAGE OF **1,891** UNITS PER YEAR

FOR THE LAST ⟨20⟩ YEARS.

MEANWHILE, THE US CENSUS

ESTIMATES THAT THE CITY'S POPULATION GREW BY **65,652** PEOPLE FROM 2010 TO 2016 ALONE.

YOU CAN SEE THESE FACTIONS ENGAGING IN BEHAVIOR THAT MIGHT SEEM ABSURD IN THE CONTEXT OF A HOUSING SHORTAGE.

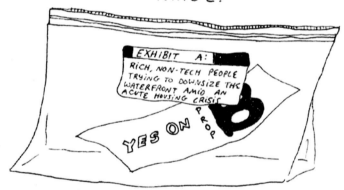

EXHIBIT A:
RICH, NON-TECH PEOPLE TRYING TO DOWNSIZE THE WATERFRONT AMID AN ACUTE HOUSING CRISIS

YES ON PROP B

ON THE BALLOT IN JUNE 2014 WAS AN INITIATIVE THAT WOULD REQUIRE VOTERS TO

INDIVIDUALLY APPROVE HEIGHT LIMIT EXEMPTIONS FOR DEVELOPMENTS ON THE CITY'S WATERFRONT.

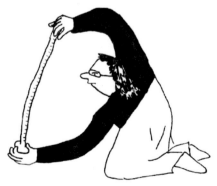

B JEOPARDIZED THREE MAJOR PROJECTS INCLUDING THE

WARRIOR'S STADIUM & A PLAN TO TURN PIER 70 INTO A MIXED-USE DEVELOPMENT

WITH OFFICE SPACE & APARTMENTS

THOSE DEVELOPMENTS WERE SLATED TO DELIVER AS MUCH AS **3,690** HOUSING UNITS

& $124 MILLION IN AFFORDABLE HOUSING FEES, ACCORDING TO DIRECTOR OF SF's DEPT. OF ELECTIONS. **JOHN ARNTZ**

THE INITIATIVE WAS FUNDED OVERWHELMINGLY BY A *NON-TECH* COUPLE, **BARBARA & RICHARD STEWART,** WHO GAVE

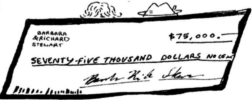

BARBARA & RICHARD STEWART — $75,000. — SEVENTY-FIVE THOUSAND DOLLARS NO CENTS

IT WAS OVERWHELMINGLY EXPECTED TO PASS, SO THE MAYOR DIDN'T EVEN TAKE A POSITION ON IT.

WOULD YOU LIKE FREE ICE CREAM? SAN FRANCISCO?

IS HOW ONE POLITICAL CONSULTANT SUMMED UP PROP. B'S VOTER APPEAL

WHY, YES I WOULD!

(IT PASSED.)

WHY VOTE AGAINST SOMETHING WHERE 60 to 70% ARE GOING TO VOTE WITH THE OTHER SIDE?

 THIS IS NOT FREE ICE CREAM.

EXHIBIT B

PROTESTS AGAINST NEW HOUSING DEVELOPMENTS THAT DON'T GET RID OF ANY EXISTING HOUSING

YOU'LL END UP SEEING PROTESTS LIKE THIS ONE AGAINST A PROPOSED CONDOMINIUM THAT WOULD REPLACE A WALGREENS & A BURGER KING.

IT DIDN'T REMOVE ANY EXISTING HOUSING OR DIRECTLY DISPLACE ANYONE.

 AT THIS MIGHT NOT MAKE SENSE.

BUT THERE ARE A COUPLE REASONS
THAT THIS HAPPENS

ONE 1 IS THAT

gentrification

WIDENS THE GAP
BETWEEN MARKET-RATE & RENT-CONTROLLED
RENTS,

MARKET RATE RENT

GENTRIFICATION

RENT CONTROLLED RENT

STRENGTHENING THE
FINANCIAL INCENTIVE
FOR LANDLORDS TO
EVICT LONGTIME TENANTS

TWO 2 IS THAT NEIGHBORHOOD ORGANIZATIONS REPRESENTING HISTORICALLY DISENFRANCHISED GROUPS HAVE USED SAN FRANCISCO'S BYZANTINE PLANNING PROCESS TO WIN CONCESSIONS FROM THE CITY'S DEVELOPMENT ELITE FOR THE LAST 30 to 40 YEARS.

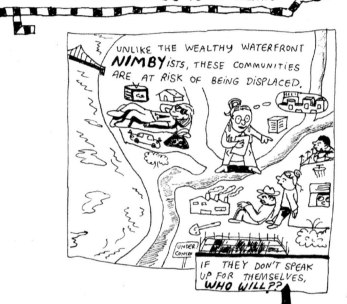

IN PRINCIPLE, IT'S FINE TO USE THE LEVERS OF

TO REDISTRIBUTE THE WEALTH AN ECONOMIC BOOM CREATES IN SAN FRANCISCO.

BUT THESE CONCESSIONS ARE BEING NEGOTIATED

 BY

WHICH SLOWS THE CITY'S ABILITY
TO PRODUCE HOUSING - BOTH
MARKET-RATE & AFFORDABLE - AT SCALE.

MAYOR **ED LEE** & OTHERS ARE TRYING
TO SPEED THIS UP, BY
GIVING AFFORDABLE HOUSING
PROJECTS FIRST PRIORITY IN
THE DEPARTMENT'S
APPROVAL PROCESS,
FOLLOWED BY MARKET-RATE
PROJECTS WITH A
HIGHER INCLUSIONARY
PERCENTAGE OF
BELOW-MARKET-RATE HOUSING.

AFFORDABLE
HOUSING

BELOW-MARKET RATE

MARKET-RATE

LUXURY

IT'S A GOOD FIRST STEP

BUT...

SF's PLANNING PROCESS IS DELIBERATELY
BUREAUCRATIC (OR HIGHLY PARTICIPATORY!)
FOR POLITICAL REASONS

Below: Actual permit process flowchart from SF Planning Department Website

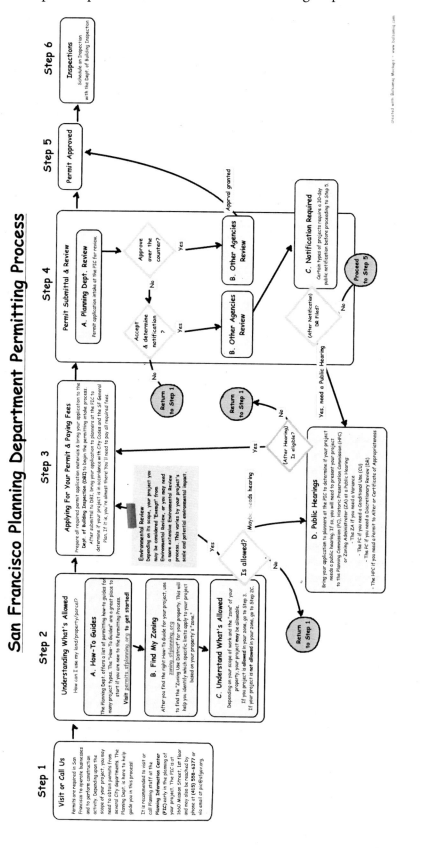

San Francisco Planning Department Permitting Process

ONE OF THE THINGS THAT MAKES
HOUSING DEVELOPMENT DIFFERENT
IN **SAN FRANCISCO** COMPARED TO
OTHER MAJOR U.S. CITIES

IS THAT BUILDING PERMITS ARE

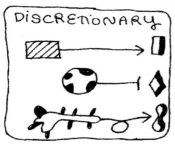

RATHER THAN

IN OTHER CITIES, IF A DEVELOPER
ALREADY MATCHES THE EXISTING
ZONING & HEIGHT RESTRICTIONS
OF THE CITY PLAN

THEY GET ISSUED A PERMIT RELATIVELY QUICKLY.

THERE'S A

WHICH CAN TAKE 6 MONTHS.

THEN, THERE ARE ALSO CHANCES FOR YOUR NEIGHBORS TO APPEAL YOUR PERMIT ON EITHER AN

ENTITLEMENT OR ENVIRONMENTAL BASIS.

THE CITY ALSO REQUIRES EXTENSIVE PUBLIC NOTICE OF PROPOSED PROJECTS, EVEN IF THEY ALREADY MEET NEIGHBORHOOD PLANS, WHICH HAVE TAKEN SEVERAL YEARS OF DELIBERATION TO PRODUCE.

PUBLIC NOTICE OF PROJECT

NEIGHBORS CAN APPEAL YOUR PROJECT FOR SOMETHING AS INSIGNIFICANT AS A

 SHADE OF PAINT, ALTHOUGH THE CITY'S PLANNING DEPARTMENT TRIES TO GET THROUGH MINOR APPEALS FAIRLY QUICKLY

 **IF THOSE FAIL** NEIGHBORHOOD GROUPS CAN ALSO FILE AN ENVIRONMENTAL LAWSUIT

OR  CEQA

(CALIFORNIA ENVIRONMENTAL QUALITY ACT)

CHALLENGING THE ENVIRONMENTAL IMPACT OF THE PROJECT.

IT ALSO MEANS THAT DEVELOPERS HAVE PROBLEMS ATTRACTING CAPITAL FINANCING IN WEAKER ECONOMIC YEARS BECAUSE OF THE POLITICAL UNCERTAINTY AROUND GETTING A PROJECT PASSED...

THE SOPHISTICATION WITH WHICH NEIGHBORHOOD GROUPS WIELD SAN FRANCISCO'S ARCANE LAND-USE & ZONING REGULATIONS FOR ACTIVIST PURPOSES IS ONE OF THE VERY UNIQUE THINGS ABOUT THE CITY'S POLITICS.

BUT THE CITY'S LEADERSHIP DOESN'T WANT TO CHANGE IT, BECAUSE IT FEARS BACKLASH FROM NEIGHBORHOOD GROUPS, WHICH ACTUALLY **DELIVER VOTES**.

KELSEY WEIGHS IN

THEY SEE THEIR POWER

VOTES

NEIGHBORHOOD GROUPS

5. ALSO, PARTS OF THE PROGRESSIVE COMMUNITY DON'T BELIEVE IN **SUPPLY + DEMAND.**

YEAH, I WAS SURPRISED BY THIS.

KIM-MAI CUTLER

"WE CAN'T BUILD OUR WAY TO AFFORDABILITY" is A COMMON REFRAIN.

TIM REDMOND, WHO USED TO EDIT THE SAN FRANCISCO BAY GUARDIAN, EVEN SUGGESTED THAT THE GOVERNMENT SHOULD TAKE **60%** OF THE CITY'S PRIVATE HOUSING OFF THE MARKET OVER THE NEXT 20 YEARS.

I HAVE NO IDEA HOW YOU WOULD FUND THIS

SF CONTROLLER SHOWS "SUPPLY AND DEMAND" DOES NOT WORK IN THE SAN FRANCISCO HOUSING MARKET. CALVIN WELCH

SEVERAL ACTIVISTS ALSO SENT ME THIS PAPER BY **CALVIN WELCH** OF THE COUNCIL OF COMMUNITY HOUSING ORGANIZATIONS

ADMIRABLY, WELCH HAS BEEN FIGHTING FOR AFFORDABLE HOUSING IN SAN FRANCISCO FOR THE LAST 40 YEARS & IS PART OF THE POLITICALLY POWERFUL

HAIGHT ASHBURY
NEIGHBORHOOD COUNCIL

WHICH HAS SEEN THAT NEIGHBORHOOD THROUGH, WELL, EVERYTHING.

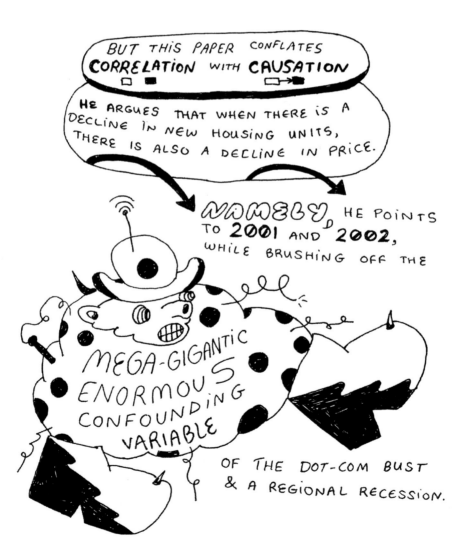

BUT THIS PAPER CONFLATES **CORRELATION** WITH **CAUSATION**

HE ARGUES THAT WHEN THERE IS A DECLINE IN NEW HOUSING UNITS, THERE IS ALSO A DECLINE IN PRICE.

NAMELY, HE POINTS TO 2001 AND 2002, WHILE BRUSHING OFF THE

MEGA-GIGANTIC ENORMOUS CONFOUNDING VARIABLE

OF THE DOT-COM BUST & A REGIONAL RECESSION.

6 ok, **CLARIFICATION:**
AFFORDABLE HOUSING ADVOCATES **WOULD** SUPPORT DEVELOPMENT IF IT HAD A MEANINGFUL SHARE OF **BELOW-MARKET-RATE** HOUSING

I MET WITH **WELCH** & HE MADE SOME GOOD POINTS. (HE'S BEEN WORKING ON THIS FOR 40 YEARS)

HIS ORGANIZATION, THE **Council of Community Housing Organizations**

"THE VOICE OF SAN FRANCISCO'S AFFORDABLE HOUSING MOVEMENT" | SFCCHO.ORG

ARGUES THAT RAW, ADDITIONAL CONSTRUCTION WILL <u>NOT</u> MAKE HOUSING MORE AFFORDABLE FOR WORKING-CLASS OR LOWER-INCOME **SAN FRANCISCANS**

LEFT TO ITS OWN DEVICES, THE MARKET WILL ONLY PRODUCE HOUSING THAT CHASES THE RICHEST BUYERS.

IN TIMES OF RISING INEQUALITY, THOSE MARKET RATE UNITS ARE INCREASINGLY OUT OF REACH FOR EVEN MIDDLE CLASS SAN FRANCISCANS.

THE ISSUE WITH INCLUSIONARY
HOUSING IS THAT CONSTRUCTION
COSTS ARE SO HIGH in SF

~$7-800,000 / 800 SQ. FT.
UNIT

THAT AFFORDABLE HOUSING REQUIRES
GENEROUS PUBLIC SUBSIDIES.*

* Or demands private subsidies which must be paid through increased prices for market rate housing.

CONSTRUCTION & LAND COSTS
ARE CHEAPER ACROSS THE
REST OF CALIFORNIA,
BUT EVEN THEN, BUILDING

BELOW-MARKET-RATE
AFFORDABLE HOUSING
←-|||-AT-SCALE-|||-→
IS PROHIBITIVELY
EXPENSIVE.

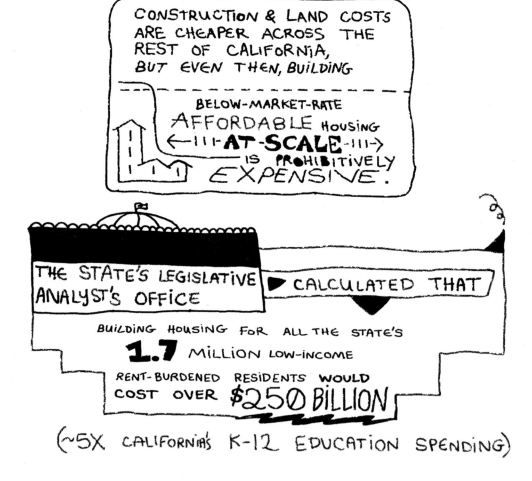

THE STATE'S LEGISLATIVE
ANALYST'S OFFICE ▶ CALCULATED THAT

BUILDING HOUSING FOR ALL THE STATE'S
1.7 MILLION LOW-INCOME
RENT-BURDENED RESIDENTS WOULD
COST OVER $250 BILLION

(~5X CALIFORNIA'S K-12 EDUCATION SPENDING)

~$274 MIL

COMING FROM THE CITY

THE REMAINING $550.3 MIL NEEDS TO COME FROM SOMEWHERE ELSE.

THE FEDERAL & STATE GOVERNMENTS USED TO HELP WITH THIS

BUT THEIR ASSISTANCE HAS DROPPED OFF GREATLY SINCE THE 1980s.

OPERA

(CUTS TO THE FEDERAL HOUSING & URBAN DEVELOPMENT DEPT. BUDGET BY REAGAN COINCIDED WITH THE RISE OF URBAN HOMELESSNESS IN SAN FRANCISCO

WHEN BELOW-MARKET-RATE UNITS DO GET BUILT, THE LINES ARE MASSIVE

2,800 PEOPLE APPLIED FOR THE 60 UNITS IN A SOMA AFFORDABLE HOUSING DEVELOPMENT AT 474 NATOMA.

ALSO, INCLUSIONARY HOUSING HAS ITS OWN TRADEOFFS.

IT CAN PASS THE COSTS OF BUILDING BELOW-MARKET-RATE UNITS ONTO MARKET-RATE BUYERS.

PAY UP

HENCE,

ANOTHER REASON FOR THE DISAPPEARANCE OF SAN FRANCISCO'S MIDDLE CLASS

PRO-DEVELOPMENT ADVOCATES
LIKE THE NONPROFIT **SPUR**
TEND TO SAY

MARKET-RATE CONSTRUCTION
WILL ALLEVIATE DEMAND
FOR THE CITY'S EXISTING
HOUSING STOCK

THEY STILL SUPPORT
INCLUSIONARY HOUSING
THOUGH

MEANWHILE

JANE KIM

WHO REPRESENTS THE TENDERLOIN,
PUSHED LEGISLATION THAT
AIMS FOR A RATIO OF

30%
BELOW-MARKET-RATE   &

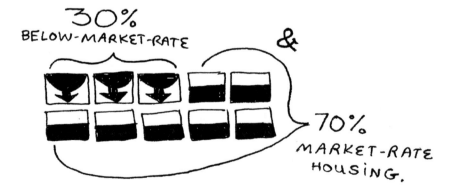

70%
MARKET-RATE
HOUSING.

SPUR SAYS THAT RATIO MEANS THE MATH WILL NO LONGER WORK OUT FOR DEVELOPERS,

MEANING THEY'LL LOSE MONEY BY DEFAULT,

SO THEY WON'T BUILD AT ALL.

OVER THE PAST DECADE, THE CITY HAD CAREFULLY NEGOTIATED

A REQUIREMENT THAT DEVELOPERS EITHER:

BUILD

12% AFFORDABLE HOUSING ON-SITE

OR

20% AFFORDABLE HOUSING OFF-SITE

OR

EQUIVALENT OF 20% INTO A CITY FUND

(PROP C RAISED THE AFFORDABILITY PERCENTAGE TO 25% IN 2016. THE CITY IS CONTINOUSLY DEBATING THE APPROPRIATE LEVELS)

THE MAGIC RATIO %

IS HARD TO FIND, AND IT SHIFTS CONSTANTLY, DEPENDING ON THE STATE OF THE HOUSING MARKET & CONSTRUCTION COSTS.

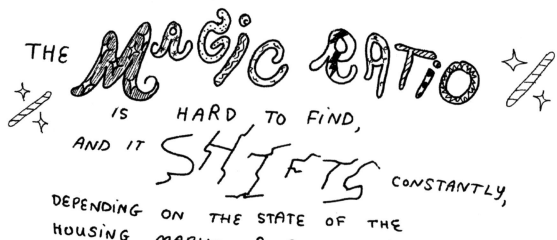

YET WE'RE ARGUING OVER SHADES OF GRAY

SORRY, SUPPLY & DEMAND STILL TOT-ALLY MATTER

MORE CONSTRUCTION CAN MAKE PRICES GO *DOWN*, AND DEFINITELY PREVENT THEM FROM

SKYROCKETING

IF YOU

LOOK AT THIS 👀👀 TRULIA STUDY | OF HOUSING PRODUCTION & PRICES SINCE 1990 IN 10 OF THE U.S.'s BIGGEST TECH HUBS,

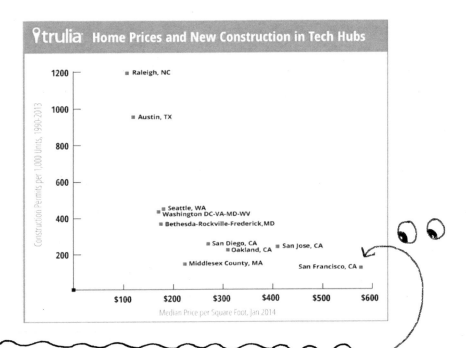

♀trulia Home Prices and New Construction in Tech Hubs

(Construction Permits per 1,000 Units, 1990-2013)

- Raleigh, NC — 1200
- Austin, TX — ~975
- Seattle, WA — ~450
- Washington DC-VA-MD-WV — ~430
- Bethesda-Rockville-Frederick, MD — ~370
- San Diego, CA — ~270
- Oakland, CA — ~250
- San Jose, CA — ~270
- Middlesex County, MA — ~150
- San Francisco, CA — ~130

Median Price per Square Foot, Jan 2014

YOU'LL SEE THAT SAN FRANCISCO HAD THE <u>HIGHEST</u> MEDIAN PRICES PER SQ. FT., AND HAD THE <u>LOWEST</u> ↓ NUMBER OF NEW CONSTRUCTION PERMITS PER 1,000 UNITS BETWEEN 1990 & 2013.

THERE ARE ALSO MANY LONG-TERM STUDIES FROM ECONOMISTS LIKE EDWARD GLAESER OF HARVARD UNIVERSITY AND JOSEPH GYOURKO OF UNIVERSITY OF PENNSYLVANIA EXAMINING THE IMPACT OF LAND-USE RESTRICTIONS & ZONING ON U.S. HOME PRICES IN DESIRABLE AREAS LIKE BOSTON, NEW YORK & COASTAL CALIFORNIA SINCE 1950

THEY FOUND THAT
IN MOST PARTS OF THE
COUNTRY

HOME PRICES ARE
AT OR **NEAR**
THE RAW COSTS
OF CONSTRUCTION.
(AS OF FEBRUARY 2017
THE MEDIAN U.S.
HOME PRICE IS
$261,800).

BUT IN PLACES WHERE ZONING REGULATIONS CREATE ARTIFICIAL LIMITS ON HOME PRODUCTION, THE FINAL PRICES TO HOMEBUYERS JUMP FAR ABOVE CONSTRUCTION COSTS.

YOU CAN ALSO LOOK AT
HISTORICAL PRODUCTION LEVELS
IN NEW YORK CITY & CALIFORNIA

Housing stock growth

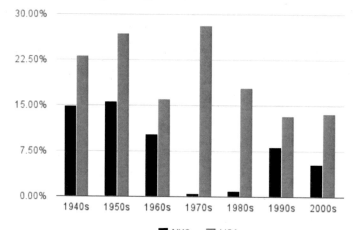

NYC ■   USA ■

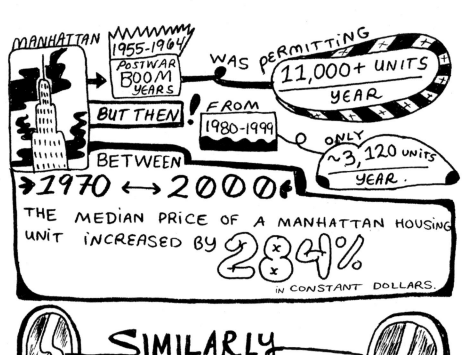

MANHATTAN 1955-1964 POSTWAR **BOOM** YEARS WAS PERMITTING **11,000+ UNITS** YEAR

BUT THEN! FROM 1980-1999 ONLY ~3,120 UNITS YEAR.

BETWEEN →1970 ←→ 2000←

THE MEDIAN PRICE OF A MANHATTAN HOUSING UNIT INCREASED BY **284%** IN CONSTANT DOLLARS.

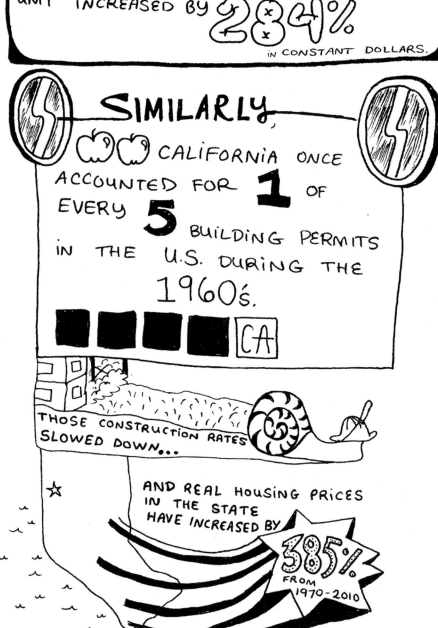

SIMILARLY,

CALIFORNIA ONCE ACCOUNTED FOR **1** OF EVERY **5** BUILDING PERMITS IN THE U.S. DURING THE 1960's.

CA

THOSE CONSTRUCTION RATES SLOWED DOWN...

AND REAL HOUSING PRICES IN THE STATE HAVE INCREASED BY **385%** FROM 1970-2010

HERE IS A SIMILAR HISTORICAL CHART FOR SAN FRANCISCO HOUSING PRODUCTION.

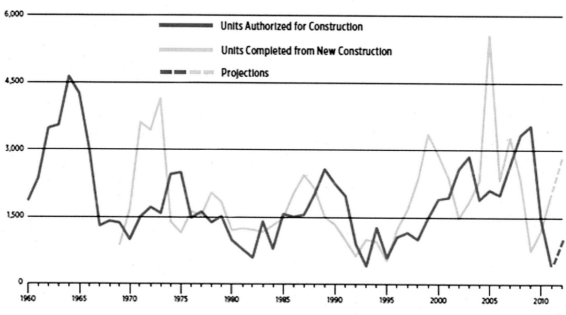

Units Authorized for Construction

Units Completed from New Construction

Projections

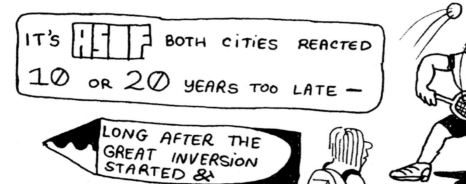

IT'S AS IF BOTH CITIES REACTED 10 OR 20 YEARS TOO LATE —

OOF

LONG AFTER THE GREAT INVERSION STARTED &

BEFORE ANYBODY HAD ANY IDEA HOW BIG THIS MIGRATION WOULD BECOME.

SUBURBIA

URBAN CORE

THIS ISSUE IS PROFOUND.

ALL WORKERS BY CREATING MORE JOBS THROUGHOUT THE ECONOMY,

SUPPORTING LOCAL BUSINESSES

&

BRINGING IN MORE TAX REVENUE FOR PUBLIC SERVICES.

EVEN IF MOST PEOPLE IN THE BAY AREA DON'T HAVE TECH JOBS, THEY WOULD GET MANY MORE OPPORTUNITIES THAN IF THERE WERE, SAY, NO ECONOMIC GROWTH.

THE POINT IS:

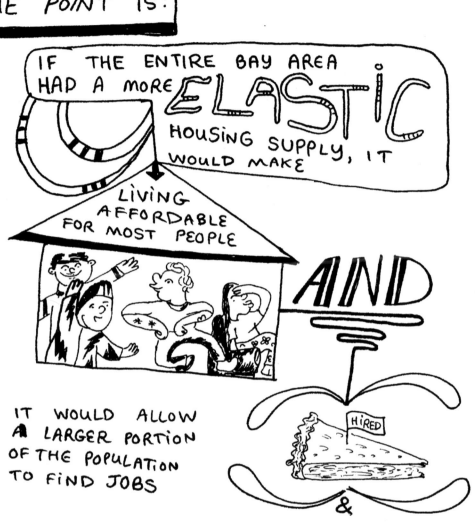

IF THE ENTIRE BAY AREA HAD A MORE **ELASTIC** HOUSING SUPPLY, IT WOULD MAKE LIVING AFFORDABLE FOR MOST PEOPLE

IT WOULD ALLOW A LARGER PORTION OF THE POPULATION TO FIND JOBS

AND

HIRED

&

AND DO THINGS LIKE

SPEND OR SAVE MONEY

INSTEAD OF MOVING FAR AWAY

& SPENDING $ ON DRIVING,

OR EVEN BEING UNEMPLOYED

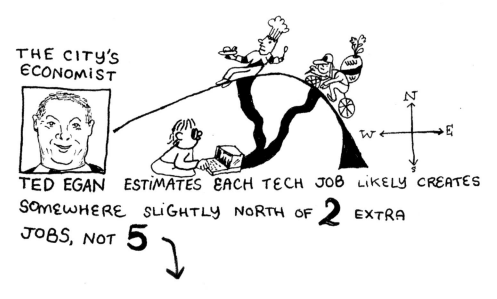

THE CITY'S ECONOMIST

TED EGAN ESTIMATES EACH TECH JOB LIKELY CREATES SOMEWHERE SLIGHTLY NORTH OF **2** EXTRA JOBS, NOT **5**

While Still a Small Industry, Tech's Multiplier Effects Are Responsible for Virtually All of the City's Employment Growth since 2010

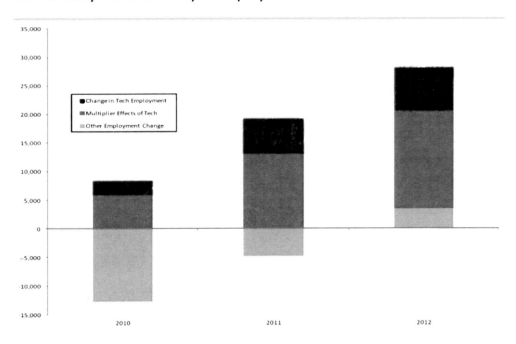

HOWEVER IT'S HARD TO HAVE EVEN BASIC DEBATES OVER MODEST INCREASES IN THE HOUSING SUPPLY HERE BECAUSE OF THIS

IDEOLOGICAL DISPUTE.

1978 & 1979: PROP 13 + RENT CONTROL

I KEEP COMING BACK TO THE LATE 1970'S BECAUSE THE CITY OF S.F. & THE STATE OF CALIFORNIA MADE CHOICES THAT HAVE HAD ENDURING IMPACTS ON HOUSING TO THIS DAY.

KIM-MAI CUTLER

IF SF SEEMS TORN APART BY CLASS WARFARE TODAY, IT WAS IN ALSO SOME AGO IN 1978

SOLD

A CHARISMATIC RELIGIOUS LEADER NAMED **JIM JONES** HAD WON THE FAVOR OF THE CITY'S POLITICAL ELITE, AND HELPED DELIVER THE MAYORSHIP TO **GEORGE MOSCONE.**

AMID EMERGING ALLEGATIONS OF PHYSICAL ABUSE, **JONES** & HUNDREDS OF HIS FOLLOWERS **DEFECTED** FROM SAN FRANCISCO TO GUYANA, WHERE HE SOUGHT TO BUILD A *UTOPIA*

SF

GUYANA

INSTEAD, HE CONVINCED MORE THAN **900** OF HIS FOLLOWERS, INCLUDING MOTHERS & INFANTS, TO INGEST CYANIDE MIXED WITH PUNCH IN A *MASS SUICIDE*

RIP RIP RIP RIP

IT WAS AN ENORMOUS TRAGEDY FOR THE CITY. NEARLY EVERY FAMILY IN THE BLACK FILLMORE DISTRICT LOST SOMEONE THEY KNEW IN JONESTOWN.

THEN, JUST **9** DAYS LATER, THERE WAS A

DOUBLE BLOW.

SUPERVISOR **DAN WHITE** MURDERED **MAYOR MOSCONE** AND GAY POLITICAL ICON **HARVEY MILK** IN S.F.'s CITY HALL

TENS OF THOUSANDS OF GRIEF-STRICKEN PEOPLE MARCHED DOWN MARKET STREET IN A CANDLELIGHT VIGIL.

IT WAS INTO **THIS** CHAOS THAT DIANNE FEINSTEIN STEPPED INTO POWER & ASSUMED MAYORSHIP

THE BROADER U.S. ECONOMIC PICTURE WAS **NOT** GREAT.

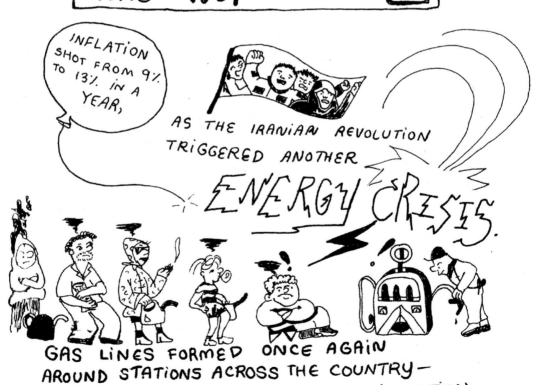

INFLATION SHOT FROM 9% TO 13% IN A YEAR,

AS THE IRANIAN REVOLUTION TRIGGERED ANOTHER ENERGY CRISIS.

GAS LINES FORMED ONCE AGAIN AROUND STATIONS ACROSS THE COUNTRY— PROMPTING ANOTHER CULTURAL RECONSIDERATION OF THE SUBURBAN IDEAL,

EARLIER IN THE SUMMER OF **1978,**

A CANTANKEROUS PUBLISHER NAMED

HOWARD JARVIS LED A

I'M MAD AS HELL

"TAXPAYER REVOLT" AS PROPERTY PRICES WERE SOARING, THREATENING TO PUSH PEOPLE OUT OF THEIR HOMES

BECAUSE OF RISING TAX BILLS.

JARVIS' IDEA WAS TO CAP PROPERTY TAXES AT **1%** OF THEIR ASSESSED VALUE

AND +

2%

PREVENT THEM FROM RISING BY MORE THAN **2%** EACH YEAR,

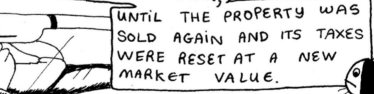

UNTIL THE PROPERTY WAS SOLD AGAIN AND ITS TAXES WERE RESET AT A NEW MARKET VALUE.

ONE ARGUMENT THAT JARVIS USED TO RALLY TENANT SUPPORT FOR *PROP. 13* WAS THAT HE PROMISED THAT LANDLORDS WOULD PASS ON THEIR TAX SAVINGS TO RENTERS.

THEY DIDNT.

THEY POCKETED THE SAVINGS FOR THEMSELVES.

TENANTS WERE FURIOUS AND RENT CONTROL MOVEMENTS ERUPTED IN AT LEAST A DOZEN CITIES THROUGHOUT CALIFORNIA FROM BERKELEY TO SANTA MONICA.

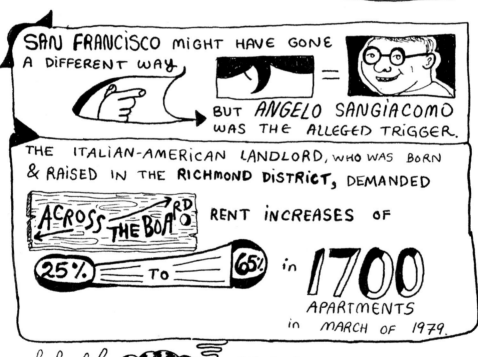

SAN FRANCISCO MIGHT HAVE GONE A DIFFERENT WAY

BUT *ANGELO SANGIACOMO* WAS THE ALLEGED TRIGGER.

THE ITALIAN-AMERICAN LANDLORD, WHO WAS BORN & RAISED IN THE RICHMOND DISTRICT, DEMANDED

ACROSS THE BOARD RENT INCREASES OF

25% TO 65% in 1700 APARTMENTS in MARCH OF 1979.

AMID THE OUTRAGE

FEINSTEIN PUSHED FOR A 40 DAY RENT FREEZE TO WARD OFF THE RISE OF A TENANT-BACKED MAYORAL CHALLENGER.

BOTH POLICIES HAVE HAD FAR-REACHING AND UNANTICIPATED CONSEQUENCES

OVERNIGHT CALIFORNIA'S PROPERTY TAX REVENUE FELL BY ALMOST 60%,

BECAUSE THE STATE'S K-12 SCHOOLS ARE FINANCED LARGELY BY PROPERTY TAXES, CALIFORNIA'S SPENDING PER STUDENT FELL FROM 5TH IN THE NATION → 50TH IN THIS DECADE.

K-12
$PROPERTY$ TAX $ $ $ $ $

WITHOUT THE ABILITY TO RELY AS HEAVILY ON PROPERTY TAXES, CITY GOVERNMENTS THROUGHOUT THE STATE HAD TO FAVOR OFFICE & RETAIL DEVELOPMENT OVER HOUSING IN ORDER TO BOOST TAX SALES.

BROOMS, INC.

GAP BRANDS! BRANDS! BRANDS! MALL OF

SOCKS ETC

IT ALSO CREATED A "LOCK-IN" EFFECT AS CALIFORNIA PROPERTY VALUES SOARED,

CREATING A BIGGER GAP IN

PROPERTY TAXES ON

NEWLY-SOLD PROPERTY

VS

PROPERTY HOMEOWNERS HELD ONTO FOR A LONG TIME

THAT RIGIDITY FURTHER ENHANCED THE POLITICAL POWER THAT NIMBY-IST HOMEOWNERS ACCUMULATED IN SUBURBAN CITY COUNCILS THROUGH THE STATE

THE MAXIMUM ALLOWABLE RENT INCREASE WENT FROM 7% TO 4% IN THE MID-80s TO A FRACTION OF THE INFLATION RATE SET BY THE RENT BOARD IN '92

SF'S 60-DAY RENT CONTROL ORDINANCE STUCK AROUND, AND WAS STRENGTHENED THROUGH THE FOLLOWING DECADES.

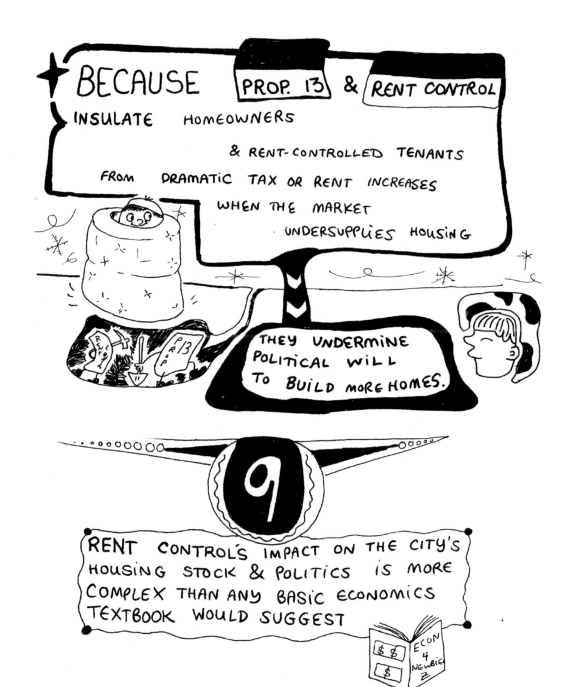

★ BECAUSE PROP. 13 & RENT CONTROL INSULATE HOMEOWNERS & RENT-CONTROLLED TENANTS FROM DRAMATIC TAX OR RENT INCREASES WHEN THE MARKET UNDERSUPPLIES HOUSING

THEY UNDERMINE POLITICAL WILL TO BUILD MORE HOMES.

9

RENT CONTROL'S IMPACT ON THE CITY'S HOUSING STOCK & POLITICS IS MORE COMPLEX THAN ANY BASIC ECONOMICS TEXTBOOK WOULD SUGGEST

RENT CONTROL IS A NATURALLY

DiViSiVE TOPIC IN THE TECH COMMUNITY

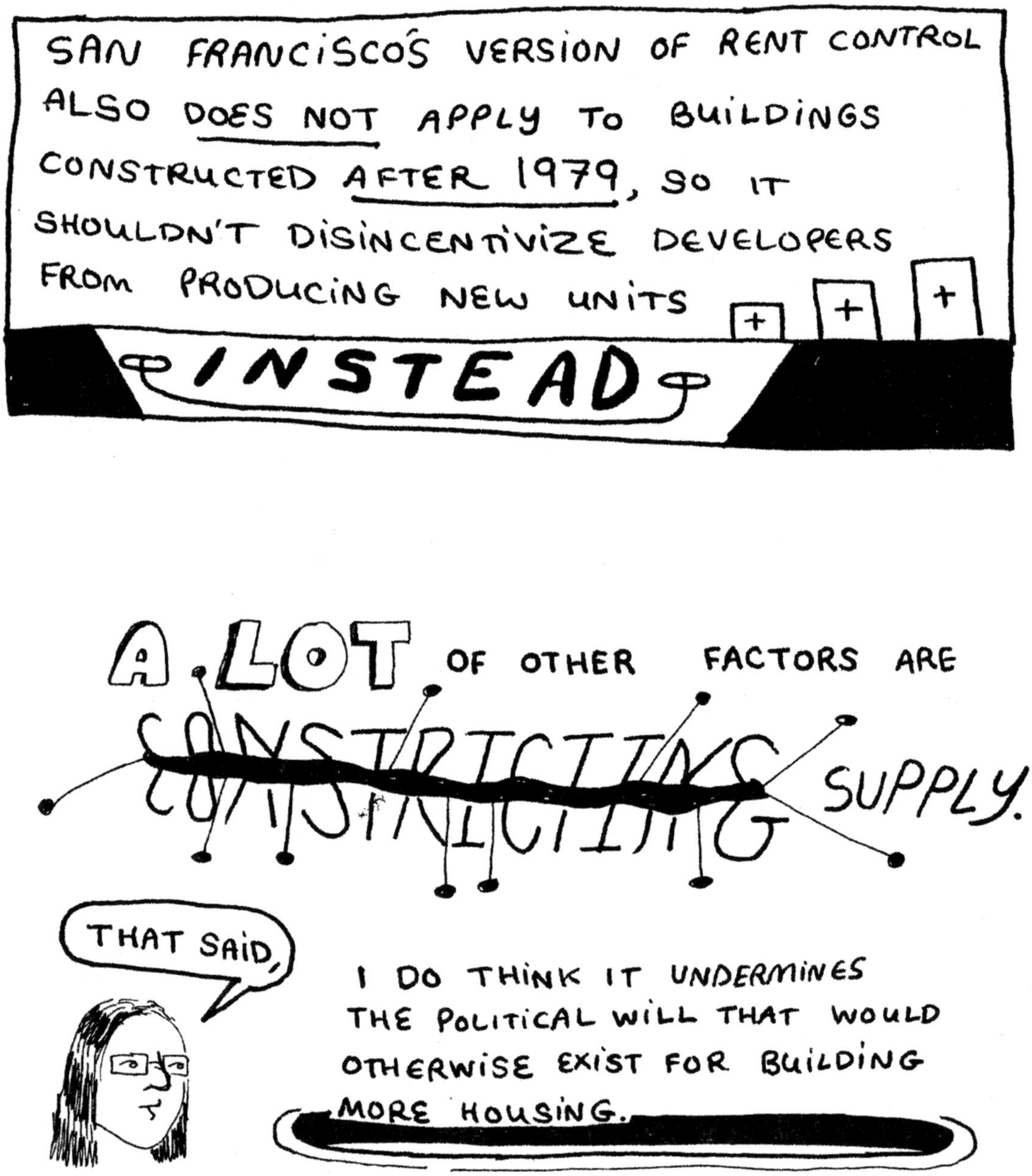

SAN FRANCISCO'S VERSION OF RENT CONTROL ALSO DOES NOT APPLY TO BUILDINGS CONSTRUCTED AFTER 1979, SO IT SHOULDN'T DISINCENTIVIZE DEVELOPERS FROM PRODUCING NEW UNITS

INSTEAD

A LOT OF OTHER FACTORS ARE ~~CONSTRICTING~~ SUPPLY.

THAT SAID

I DO THINK IT UNDERMINES THE POLITICAL WILL THAT WOULD OTHERWISE EXIST FOR BUILDING MORE HOUSING.

SO, A HIGHLY-RESTRICTED HOUSING SUPPLY **10**
+ RISING DEMAND
+ A VOLATILE LOCAL ECONOMY PRONE TO BOOMS & BUSTS
+ STRICT RENT CONTROL WITHOUT VACANCY CONTROL

= **EVICTION CRISIS EVERY DECADE !!**

LACKING VACANCY CONTROLS MEANS LANDLORDS CAN RE-SET RENTS AT WHATEVER THE MARKET WILL BEAR

RESET TO MARKET

WHEN NEW RENT-CONTROLLED TENANTS MOVE IN.

THE **LOGIC** IS THAT _WITH_ VACANCY CONTROLS, LANDLORDS WON'T INVEST IN MAINTAINING THEIR PROPERTIES.

THE **FLIPSIDE** IS THAT THE LANDLORD _ALSO_ HAS A STRONG FINANCIAL INCENTIVE TO EVICT LONGSTANDING TENANTS WHO ARE PAYING BELOW-MARKET RATES.

SO EVERY DECADE DURING A BOOM, THERE IS A TRAGIC, ELDERLY FACE FOR THE STORY OF DISPLACEMENT.

Matthew Miller bought 1506-1510 Jackson Street for $1.2 million in January 2012. Miller had used the Ellis Act before on a different property. Within four months, he began trying to displace the longtime residents at 1506-1510 Jackson. 1508-A Jackson Street was the home for Chinese immigrants Gum Gee Lee and her husband, 80-year-old Poon Heung Lee since 1979. They raised seven children there, including their 48-year-old disabled daughter. As Gum Gee Lee, 73, explained, "We raised our family here and we paid rent for more than 30 years. This new landlord knew we lived here when he bought the building. But he did not plan to keep us. He started to evict all of the tenants right away." The family lives on Social Security checks and explained that it would be nearly impossible to find anything they could afford. They wanted to stay near Chinatown where there are social support services for their daughter's disability. Before being forced out, Gum Gee Lee explained, "We thought we'd live here until we passed away, and now this. It is all so sad."

IT SUCKS. I SAT IN A HIGH SCHOOL GYM IN THE TENDERLOIN FULL OF TERRIFIED ELDERLY & DISABLED PEOPLE AT A CITYWIDE TENANT CONVENTION

(FORMER) CITY SUPERVISOR

DAVID CAMPOS

PUSHED LEGISLATION

THROUGH THE BOARD OF SUPERVISORS THAT WOULD RAISE COMPENSATION FOR ELLIS ACT EVICTEES.

IT'S GOING FROM

$5200 / TENANT

TO THE DIFFERENCE BETWEEN

THE TENANT'S CURRENT RENT

& THE MARKET-RATE RENT FOR A COMPARABLE APARTMENT OVER 2 YRS

AT CURRENT RATES, THIS WOULD BE

MORE THAN $44,832 FOR A 2-BD APT

$44,832

1   2

THEY'RE TRYING TO CHANGE THE LAW AT STATE LEVELS TOO.

MARK LENO

WHO REPRESENTED S.F. IN THE CALIFORNIA STATE SENATE

ALSO INTRODUCED A BILL

THAT WOULD REQUIRE LANDLORDS

TO HOLD A PROPERTY FOR 5 YEARS BEFORE INVOKING THE ELLIS ACT TO EVICT TENANTS

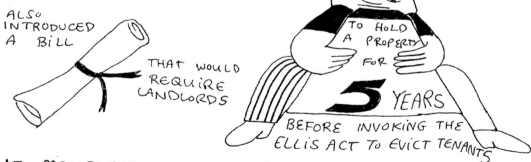

IT PASSED THE SENATE HOUSING & TRANSPORT COMMITTEE, BUT WAS TABLED IN 2015 AFTER LONG-STANDING OPPOSITION FROM REALTORS.

FUCK, THIS IS COMPLICATED.

ANTI-TECH SENTIMENT BECOMES A CATALYST

TENANTS RIGHTS ACTIVISTS HAD STRUGGLED TO

PROTECT US ELLIS ACT

NNNG

MT. PUBLIC OPINION

GENERATE MOMENTUM FOR PROTECTIONS AGAINST THE ELLIS ACT EVICTIONS

BUT VILLAINS LIKE REAL-ESTATE SPECULATORS ARE

TOO NEBULOUS

INDEED

MANY OF THE LANDLORDS RESPONSIBLE FOR THE BULK OF ELLIS ACT EVICTIONS HIDE BEHIND

STRANGELY NAMED ENTITIES LIKE

PINEAPPLE BOY, LLC.

BUT THE GOOGLE BUS PROTESTS WORKED

THEY WERE A MEDIA SENSATION

THEY TAPPED INTO THIS INCHOATE
SENSE OF FRUSTRATION AROUND EVERYTHING
FROM :

RISING INCOME INEQUALITY

TO PRIVACY

TO SURVEILLANCE

TO THE ENVIRONMENTAL IMPACT OF THE HARDWARE WE BUY

TO A DUBIOUS SENSE THAT TODAY'S LEADING TECH COMPANIES AREN'T LIVING UP TO THEIR MISSIONS OF NOT BEING EVIL.*

KRUSTY'S KORNER
ALPHABET DROPPED THE "DON'T BE EVIL" CLAUSE FROM ITS CODE OF CONDUCT IN OCTOBER 2015

ORGANIZER

THE "WE-HATE-TECH-WORKERS" IS MOSTLY A MEDIA NARRATIVE.

IT'S NOT ABOUT THAT.

FRED SHERBURN-ZIMMER

IT'S ABOUT INCOME DISPARITY

ITS ABOUT SPECULATORS USING HIGH-INCOME WORKERS TO DISPLACE COMMUNITIES

AFFORDABLE HOUSING NOW!

WARNING
ILLEGAL USE OF PUBLIC INFRASTRUCTURE

13. WHO ARE THE PROTESTERS AND WHAT DO THEY WANT?

LIKE THE TECH COMMUNITY ITSELF, THE ACTIVIST COMMUNITY IS PRETTY

HETEROGENEOUS

CAUSA JUSTA JUST CAUSE

THERE ARE GROUPS LIKE CAUSA JUSTA, WHICH FOCUSES ON BLACK & LATINO COMMUNITIES

OR HOUSING FOCUSED GROUPS LIKE THE HOUSING RIGHTS COMMITTEE

& OTHERS AFFILIATED WITH THE SF TENANTS UNION

& THE ANTI-EVICTION MAPPING PROJECT, WHICH ASKS PEOPLE TO BOYCOTT RENTING FROM ELLIS ACT EVICTION PROPERTIES

THE BROAD POINT HERE IS:

WHILE TECH-FUELED ECONOMIC GROWTH CAN BE GOOD,

FOR SALE

ARTISANA

GENTRIFICATION CARRIES ENORMOUS & OFTEN TRAGIC COSTS FOR CERTAIN INDIVIDUALS & COMMUNITIES

IF THOSE COSTS AREN'T RECOGNIZED BY A PURELY MARKET-BASED SYSTEM, **THEN THE POLITICAL SYSTEM SHOULD RECTIFY IT.**

ERIN McELROY OF THE ANTI-EVICTION MAPPING PROJECT

WE IMPLORE TECH TO START TALKING TO US.

COME OUT INTO THE STREETS WITH US.

I DON'T THINK IT OCCURS TO PEOPLE THEY CAN BE A BODY TOO. PEOPLE LIVE IN BUBBLES HERE.

IF YOU'RE SCARED, WHAT DOES THAT COMPARE TO PEOPLE WHO ARE BEING FORCED OUT OF THEIR HOMES?

BUT THERE ARE TIMES WHEN IT CAN JUST GET WEIRD OR BORDERLINE DISTURBING

THE COUNTERFORCE LEFT CREEPY FLYERS OUTSIDE OF TECH ENTREPRENEUR KEVIN ROSE'S HOUSE DEMANDING $3 BILLION FOR AN ANARCHIST UTOPIA

KEVIN ROSE ☺ = ☺ PARASITE

AND SHOWED UP ONE MORNING AT THE BERKELEY HOME OF GOOGLE ENGINEERING MANAGER ANTHONY LEVANDOWSKI

AND IT OFTEN FEELS LIKE PROTESTS MEANT TO STIR MEANINGFUL QUESTIONS ABOUT INCOME EQUALITY, GENTRIFICATION & HOUSING

STOP TECH

VEER OFF INTO MISGUIDED HATRED OR ANGER

HOWEVER

AT A NON-VIOLENT PROTEST, THERE WERE CHILDREN, PARENTS & TEACHERS IN THE STREET WITH A BRASS BAND.

AT THE PROTEST:

HIGH SCHOOL STUDENT NATALIA ARGUELLO-INGLIS:

WE CAN'T BLINDLY HATE ON THE TECHIES & YUPPIES. WHO ARE WE TO JUDGE WHO CAN COME INTO THIS CITY & WHO CANNOT? GENTRIFICATION IS NOT GOING TO GO AWAY. BUT WE CAN WORK WITH THE PEOPLE WHO ARE CAUSING IT.

BUT THERE WAS ALSO THIS SIGN

TECH=DEATH

WHICH IS A REFERENCE TO THE EARLY 1990S ANTI-AIDS DOCUMENTARY

SILENCE=DEATH

AT LEAST THREE PROTESTS INDIVIDUALLY TARGETED GOOGLE EMPLOYEES

KEVIN ROSE: PARASITE!

GREETINGS. YOUR NEIGHBOR IS A PARASITE. PERHAPS NOT OF YOU, BUT OF US. THIS IS WHY WE ARE HERE

JACK HALPRIN
GOOGLE LAWYER

GOOGLE STOP JACK HALPRIN FROM EVICTING TEACHERS

WHO WAS EVICTING MULTIPLE TENANTS FROM HIS HOUSE ON GUERRERO ST.

FOLLOWING THE PROTESTS, A BUSINESS INSIDER REPORTER, KYLE RUSSELL HAD HIS GOOGLE GLASS RIPPED OFF & SMASHED

ALSO, A PROTESTER CLIMBED ON TOP OF A YAHOO BUS & VOMITED ON IT.

RANDY SHAW HOUSES LOW-INCOME SAN FRANCISCANS IN 1,600 UNITS UNDER THE NON-PROFIT TENDERLOIN HOUSING CLINIC, AND SEES THIS AS A NEW FORM OF NATIVISM.

WHEN HE MOVED HERE IN THE LATE-1970's, HE REMEMBERED STRAIGHT RESIDENTS MAKING THE SAME COMPLAINTS ABOUT AN INFLUX OF GAYS INTO THE CASTRO, OR A FLOOD OF LATINO IMMIGRANTS INTO WHAT WAS A LARGELY IRISH-AMERICAN MISSION DISTRICT A GENERATION AGO

THE WAR ON TECH WORKERS—AS OPPOSED TO TECH COMPANIES OR POLICIES—IS NOT REALLY A "CLASS WAR".

RATHER, IT IS ABOUT ONE GROUP OF PREDOMINANTLY WHITE PEOPLE COMPLAINING ABOUT A SIMILAR DEMOGRAPHIC THAT LIKES MANY OF THE SAME RESTAURANTS, BARS, STREET FESTIVALS, AND SAMBA CLASSES THAT THEY DO— BUT WHO MAKES MORE MONEY

SHAW POINTS OUT THAT MANY OF THE UNION-AFFILIATING PROTESTERS BLASTING TWITTER'S HEADQUARTERS

ARE SIMULTANEOUSLY REQUESTING BUDGET INCREASES FROM THE MAYOR'S OFFICE

WHICH IS LARGELY POSSIBLE BECAUSE OF THE TECH-FUELED ECONOMIC BOOM

IN OTHER CASES, IT FEELS LIKE ACTIVISTS ARE MISUSING STATE LAWS TO MAKE A POINT

SEVERAL GROUPS SPENT 8 HOURS AT THE BOARD OF SUPERVISORS MEETING IN APRIL 2014

OR JUST USING?

THEY WERE CHALLENGING THE CITY'S DECISION NOT TO PUT THE NEW SHUTTLE PILOT PROGRAM UNDER ENVIRONMENTAL REVIEW VIA CEQA

EVEN THOUGH BUSES TAKE AS MANY AS 4,000 COMMUTERS OFF THE ROAD A DAY

THEY ARGUED THAT DISPLACEMENT OF EXISTING COMMUNITIES SHOULD BE COUNTED AS AN ENVIRONMENTAL IMPACT

WE'RE NOT SAYING NO BUSES

WE'RE SAYING THAT THERE ARE CONSEQUENCES WHEN THESE BUSES MOVE INTO THE NEIGHBORHOOD

FRED SHERBURN-ZIMMER

IN 2014

THE CITY WAS CHARGING $1 PER BUS STOP, WHICH CERTAINLY IS LOW WHEN THE REGULAR MUNI FARE IS $2

BUT UNDER CA PROPOSITION 218 THE TRANSPORTATION AGENCY IS NOT ALLOWED TO CREATE A REVENUE-GENERATING PROGRAM.

SO THE CITY COULD ONLY PAY FOR ITS $1.7 MILLION IN COSTS

GOOGLE TRIED TO RECTIFY THE SITUATION IN AN UNORTHODOX WAY

BY DONATING $6.8 MILLION FOR FREE RIDES ON MUNI FOR LOW-INCOME YOUTH

ERIN McELROY

GOOGLE NEVER CAME TO US & ASKED WHAT WE WOULD LIKE TO SEE

WE ARE NOT INTO BACKDOOR DEAL-MAKING WITH POLITICIANS

& NONE OF THIS AMOUNTS TO MASSIVE, SYSTEMS-LEVEL CHANGE. IT PROTECTS LONG-TIME RESIDENTS, BUT DOESN'T MAKE SF MORE AFFORDABLE OR AVAILABLE TO FUTURE MIDDLE OR WORKING-CLASS RESIDENTS

WE'RE PLAYING FASTBALL RIGHT NOW

THESE ARE BAND-AID SOLUTIONS

INDEED, THIS IS POLITICS!

SO COMPLICATED! WHAT ARE COMPROMISES THAT HAVE ACTUALLY WORKED?

NORMALLY, CITY POLICY MAKERS FAVOR CONSTRUCTING WHERE THERE ARE NO PRE-EXISTING UNITS

BECAUSE NEW HOUSING IS GENERALLY LESS AFFORDABLE THAN OLD HOUSING

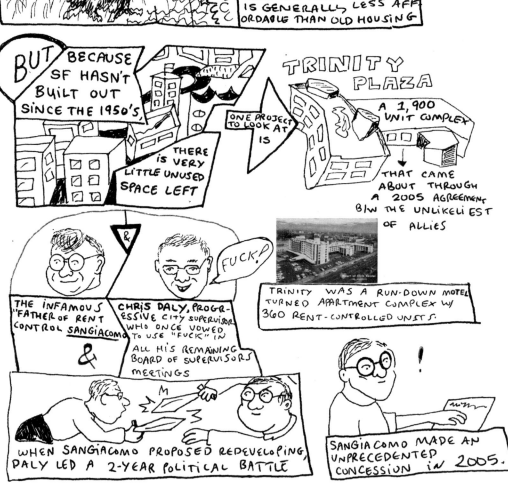

BUT BECAUSE SF HASN'T BUILT OUT SINCE THE 1950'S, THERE IS VERY LITTLE UNUSED SPACE LEFT

ONE PROJECT TO LOOK AT IS

TRINITY PLAZA

A 1,900 UNIT COMPLEX

THAT CAME ABOUT THROUGH A 2005 AGREEMENT B/W THE UNLIKELIEST OF ALLIES

FUCK!

TRINITY WAS A RUN-DOWN MOTEL TURNED APARTMENT COMPLEX W/ 360 RENT-CONTROLLED UNITS.

THE INFAMOUS "FATHER OF RENT CONTROL SANGIACOMO & CHRIS DALY, PROGRESSIVE CITY SUPERVISOR WHO ONCE VOWED TO USE "FUCK" IN ALL HIS REMAINING BOARD OF SUPERVISORS MEETINGS

WHEN SANGIACOMO PROPOSED REDEVELOPING, DALY LED A 2-YEAR POLITICAL BATTLE

SANGIACOMO MADE AN UNPRECEDENTED CONCESSION IN 2005.

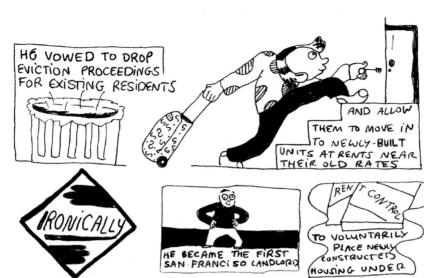

HE VOWED TO DROP EVICTION PROCEEDINGS FOR EXISTING RESIDENTS

AND ALLOW THEM TO MOVE IN TO NEWLY-BUILT UNITS AT RENTS NEAR THEIR OLD RATES

IRONICALLY

HE BECAME THE FIRST SAN FRANCISCO LANDLORD

TO VOLUNTARILY PLACE NEWLY CONSTRUCTED HOUSING UNDER RENT CONTROL

▲ IT WAS A BIG WIN ▲

LONG-TERM RESIDENTS WEREN'T DISPLACED AND GOT BRAND-NEW HOMES AT NEAR THEIR OLD RENT, PLUS THE CITY GOT TO PROVIDE MANY MORE HOMES TO OTHER SAN FRANCISCANS.

¿WHAT IS THE CITY GOVERNMENT DOING? 15

IF YOU CAN SEE ANY SILVER LINING IN BEING ANTAGONIZED EVERY DAY IN PROTESTS,

ITS THAT THE GOVERNMENT WILL BE REALLY, REALLY, REALLY FOCUSED ON HOUSING

A LOT OF THINGS THAT WEREN'T CONSIDERED POLITICALLY POSSIBLE FOR YEARS BEGAN HAPPENING

THE BOARD OF SUPERVISORS PASSED A BILL TO LEGALIZE IN-LAW UNITS

THEY VOTED TO INCREASE ELLIS ACT RELOCATION COMPENSATION — THOUGH SF LANDLORDS WITH THE SF APARTMENT ASSOCIATION WANT TO SUE.

THE MAYOR DOUBLED THE CITY'S DOWN PAYMENT ASSISTANCE FOR 1ST TIME BUYERS TO $200,000

HE PLEDGED TO BUILD OR REHABILITATE 30,000 UNITS IN THE NEXT 6 YEARS

WITH 1/3 BEING PERMANENTLY AFFORDABLE TO LOWER & MODERATE INCOME FAMILIES

HE ALSO CONVENED A WORKING GROUP

REPRESENTING 75+ DIFFERENT INTERESTS

THAT WILL COME UP WITH SOLUTIONS TO THE HOUSING CRISIS.

THERE IS NO SIWER BULLET IN ANY OF THESE.

IT'S A HARD PROBLEM.

LEE, LENO & OTHERS COLLABORATED ON THE ELLIS ACT BILL IN THE STATE LEGISLATURE.

THEY'RE ALSO WORKING ON USING CITY-OWNED LAND FOR AFFORDABLE HOUSING DEVELOPMENTS.

AHEAD OF THE PROTESTS

IN 2012, LEE GOT VOTERS TO PASS AN AFFORDABLE HOUSING TRUST FUND

BUT EVEN THESE PROJECTS ARE LIKELY TO GET MIRED IN THAT CRAZY PLANNING PROCESS

16. WHAT IS THE TECH INDUSTRY DOING?

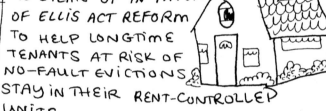

RON CONWAY ASKED TECH CEOS ACROSS THE INDUSTRY TO SPEAK UP IN FAVOR OF ELLIS ACT REFORM TO HELP LONGTIME TENANTS AT RISK OF NO-FAULT EVICTIONS STAY IN THEIR RENT-CONTROLLED UNITS

GOOGLE

GAVE $6.8 MILLION AS A TEMPORARY SOURCE OF FUNDING FOR FREE MUNI RIDES FOR LOW-INCOME YOUTH.

IN MARCH 2014 THEY OPENED A BAY AREA IMPACT CHALLENGE, GIVING 5 MILLION $5 MILLION TO 25 BAY AREA NONPROFITS

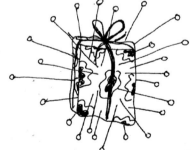

THEY ALSO FUNDED ALL THE BAY AREA'S PROJECTS ON DONORS CHOOSE, WHERE TEACHERS LIST FUNDING THEY NEED FOR CLASSROOM PROJECTS.

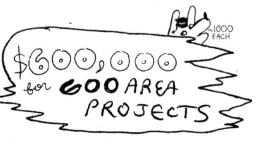

~1000 EACH

$600,000 for 600 AREA PROJECTS

SALESFORCE CEO
MARC BENIOFF

CHALLENGED TECH WORKERS TO RAISE $10 MILLION FOR ANTI-POVERTY ORGANIZATIONS, FOUNDING THE TIPPING POINT SFGIVES FUND IN THE PROCESS

THEY DID IT

10 MILLION

& WITH HIS WIFE GAVE 100 MILLION TO THE UCSF BENIOFF CHILDREN'S HOSPITAL AND ITS AFFILIATE, THE CHILDREN'S HOSPITAL & RESEARCH CENTER IN OAKLAND

THE MAYOR & SF.CITI BROKERED MEETINGS BETWEEN TECH COMPANIES LIKE JAWBONE, PINTEREST, AIRBNB & NON-PROFITS LIKE THE YMCA, THE TENDERLOIN HOUSING CLINIC & THE MISSION ECONOMIC DEVELOPMENT AGENCY.

THERE'S A LOT OF OTHER THINGS THAT I CAN'T ALL REMEMBER, LIKE **ZENDESK** & THE CITY'S

LINK-SF A MOBILE SITE FOR HOMELESS SERVICES

THERE WAS THE **HACKTIVATION FOR THE HOMELESS**

DEVELOPING APPS FOR NON-PROFITS

SQUARE DOING MID-MARKET TRASH PICKUP EVERY FRIDAY

AIRBNB IS REMITTING SAN FRANCISCO'S 14-PERCENT HOTEL OCCUPANCY TAX

CONSIDER THESE THINGS JUST A START.

WHAT ABOUT THIS **"TWITTER TAX BREAK"** THAT THE UNIONS SAY IS COSTING THE CITY **$56 MILLION**?

THERE IS A  TON OF ANGER

AT THE TECH COMMUNITY

OVER 2 TAX BREAKS FROM 2011.

DAVID CAMPOS

FORMER CITY SUPERVISOR WHO REPRESENTED THE MISSION, CALLED FOR A HEARING ON THE "TWITTER TAX BREAK"

TWITTER TAX BREAK

 ITS A COMPLICATED ISSUE

IF YOU LOOK INTO IT

Yes, SAN FRANCISCO

IS AN EXTREMELY DESIRABLE PLACE,

AND HAS MORE LEVERAGE THAN MOST CITIES IN THE ENTIRE COUNTRY

IF TWITTER HAD MOVED TO SOUTH SAN FRANCISCO IN 2011 AT THAT TIME, THE COMPANY WOULD HAVE PAID THAT CITY GOVERMENT $15 PER / EMPLOYEE / YEAR, OR $37,500 A YEAR FOR 2,500 EMPLOYEES

SO THIS UNCAPPED UNPREDICTABLE TAX LIABILITY THAT COULD STRETCH INTO millions OF DOLLARS WAS A HUGE REASON TO LEAVE, EVEN THOUGH TWITTER'S LEADERSHIP WANTED TO STAY

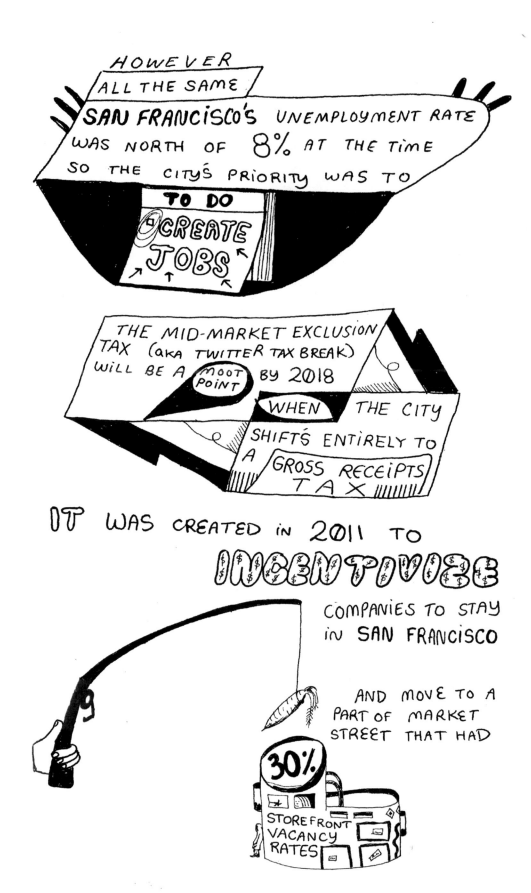

HOWEVER
ALL THE SAME

SAN FRANCISCO'S UNEMPLOYMENT RATE WAS NORTH OF 8% AT THE TIME SO THE CITY'S PRIORITY WAS TO

TO DO
☑ CREATE JOBS

THE MID-MARKET EXCLUSION TAX (aka TWITTER TAX BREAK) WILL BE A MOOT POINT BY 2018 WHEN THE CITY SHIFTS ENTIRELY TO A GROSS RECEIPTS TAX

IT WAS CREATED IN 2011 TO INCENTIVIZE

COMPANIES TO STAY IN SAN FRANCISCO

AND MOVE TO A PART OF MARKET STREET THAT HAD

30%

STOREFRONT VACANCY RATES

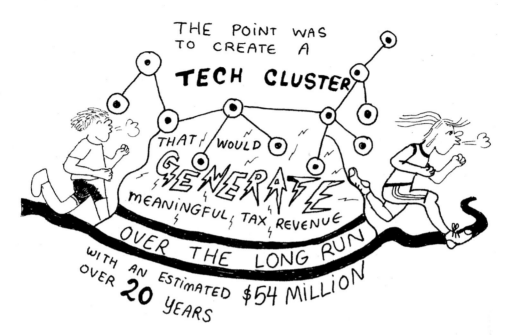

THE POINT WAS TO CREATE A **TECH CLUSTER** THAT WOULD GENERATE MEANINGFUL TAX REVENUE OVER THE LONG RUN WITH AN ESTIMATED $54 MILLION OVER **20** YEARS

& THE EXCLUSION WAS AVAILABLE TO ALL COMPANIES WITH MORE THAN

250,000 IN PAYROLLS THAT MOVED THERE.

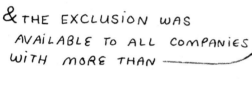

TWITTER WAS THE ANCHOR,

AND IT MOVED ITS HEADQUARTERS TO A

THAT HAD BEEN *VACANT* FOR **5** YEARS

SHORENSTEIN-OWNED SF MART BUILDING

COMPANIES LIKE **ZENDESK**, **SPOTIFY** & **ONE KINGS LANE** ALSO JOINED THE PROGRAM.

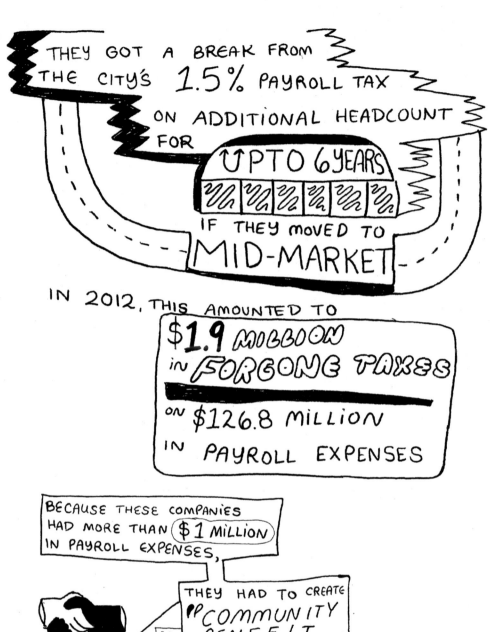

THEY GOT A BREAK FROM THE CITY'S 1.5% PAYROLL TAX ON ADDITIONAL HEADCOUNT FOR UP TO 6 YEARS IF THEY MOVED TO MID-MARKET

IN 2012, THIS AMOUNTED TO

$1.9 MILLION in FORGONE TAXES

on $126.8 MILLION IN PAYROLL EXPENSES

BECAUSE THESE COMPANIES HAD MORE THAN $1 MILLION IN PAYROLL EXPENSES,

THEY HAD TO CREATE "COMMUNITY BENEFIT AGREEMENTS"

THAT DOCUMENTED HOW THEY'RE GIVING BACK TO THE COMMUNITY THROUGH

DONATIONS

&

VOLUNTEERSHIP

WHILE THE ADVISORY COMMITTEE OVERSEEING THE PROGRAM LOVED IPO CANDIDATE ZENDESK, ITS MEMBERS ARE FRUSTRATED WITH TWITTER & OTHER COMPANIES FOR BEING TOO VAGUE ON COMMITMENTS OR NOT EVEN SHOWING UP TO MEETINGS

THEN, THE WHOLE PAYROLL TAX WAS SUBSEQUENTLY REFORMED OR SCRAPPED BY VOTERS THE FOLLOWING YEAR THROUGH PROPOSITION E

PROP E WAS

IN FAVOR OF A TAX ON
GROSS RECEIPTS
THAT'S STARTING TO BE
PHASED IN.

THE ARGUMENT WAS THAT

PAYROLL TAXES PENALIZE JOB CREATION

ON TOP OF ALL THAT THE CITY WAS ONLY COLLECTING PAYROLL TAXES FROM

LESS THAN

1 0 %
OF THE
~100,000 REGISTERED

COMPANIES
IN THE CITY
AT THAT TIME

(SF) HAD TRIED TO

SHIFT

FROM A PAYROLL TAX TO A GROSS RECEIPTS TAX BEFORE, BUT THE MEASURE DIDN'T PASS UNTIL **2012**

(SO THE TAX BREAK EVERYONE IS SCREAMING ABOUT WILL BE *IRRELEVANT* IN **2018** WHEN THE GROSS RECEIPTS TAX IS FULLY BAKED IN

2018

AND IF **SAN FRANCISCO** IS ABLE TO CONVINCE TECH COMPANIES TO STAY

AND  OF THEM

TURNS INTO A FACEBOOK, GOOGLE OR ORACLE-SIZED COMPANY, THE CITY WILL BE ABLE TO CAPTURE A PERCENTAGE OF WHAT WILL BE BILLIONS OF DOLLARS IN ANNUAL REVENUES.

IN 2014 THE CITY SAID IT HAD ALREADY HELPED GENERATE $8.4 MILLION IN

PROPERTY OR REAL ESTATE TRANSFER TAXES

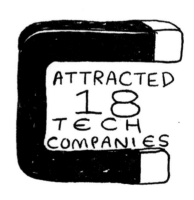

ATTRACTED 18 TECH COMPANIES

AND CONVINCED 17 SMALL BUSINESSES TO OPEN ON THE STREET

MAP OF THE EXCLUSION ZONE ←

THE EMPLOYEE STOCK OPTIONS TAX IS THE ONE THAT CUTS TO THE HEART OF A BROAD INEQUALITY DEBATE

THIS WAS THE SECOND TEMPORARY TAX EXEMPTION PASSED IN 2011

IT FOCUSED ON EMPLOYEE STOCK OPTIONS

AND WAS CREATED TO RETAIN PRE-IPO COMPANIES LIKE ZYNGA, TWITTER & ZENDESK IN SAN FRANCISCO

IT SHOULD ALSO BE OVER-RIDDEN BY THE SHIFT TO A GROSS-RECEIPTS TAX

IT IS MORE CONTROVERSIAL IN THE CONTEXT OF THE BROADER INEQUALITY DEBATE

JAMES TEMPLE

WROTE A PIECE FOR THE S.F. CHRONICLE IN 2013 SAYING THIS TAX BREAK COST THE CITY **$34 MILLION**

ON TOP OF THE PROJECTED **$22 MILLION** IN FOREGONE REVENUE FROM THE MID-MARKET PROGRAM

THIS IS WHERE THE **$56 MILLION** FIGURE COMMES FROM—

EVEN THOUGH IF TWITTER HAD MOVED,

THE CITY WOULD HAVE SEEN

NONE OF IT

IT'S PHANTOM MONEY

AT THE TIME IT WAS PASSED, SF WAS ONE OF THE FEW CITIES IN THE NATION

TO TAX EMPLOYEE STOCK OPTIONS

AND IT INCLUDED THEM IN THE 1.5% PAYROLL TAX

SEAL OF THE CITY AND COUNTY OF SAN FRANCISCO · CONTROLLER'S OFFICE

FOUND THAT SAN FRANCISCO HAD A HIGHER PROPENSITY TO LOSE BUSINESSES TO

SANTA CLARA COUNTY

SAN MATEO COUNTY

ALAMEDA COUNTY

CONTRA COSTA COUNTY

THE CITY GOVERNMENT STUDIED MORE THAN A DOZEN SF-BASED

IPOs

SINCE 1997, & FOUND THAT NO SINGLE COMPANY PAID MORE THAN $685,000 IN TAXES ON EMPLOYEE$ STOCK OPTIONS IN ANY 1 YEAR. SO THEY

CAPPED

$750,000

THE EMPLOYEE STOCK OPTIONS TAX AT $750,000 FOR PRE-IPO COMPANIES ON

EQUITY GRANTED BEFORE A PUBLIC OFFERING

 YET I CAN SEE HOW WITNESSING **HUNDREDS** OF EARLY TWITTER EMPLOYEES BECOME

KIM-MAI CUTLER

MILLIONAIRES OVERNIGHT

WOULD BE AGGRAVATING TO SAN FRANCISCANS WHO ARE FEELING

SQUEEZED OR FEEL LIKE PUBLIC SERVICES AREN'T ADEQUATELY SUPPORTED

EVERYONE IS ALSO DISTURBED BY RISING INCOME INEQUALITY

WHICH IS GROWING AT THE FASTEST RATE IN THE COUNTRY.

ACCORDING TO A 2012 BROOKINGS STUDY 2012

AT THE TIME A LOT OF VCs & FOUNDERS WERE DIGESTING THIS BOOK

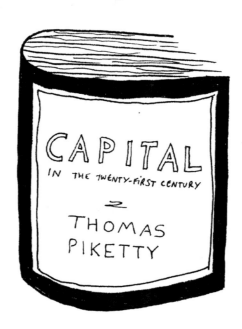

CAPITAL IN THE TWENTY-FIRST CENTURY

~

THOMAS PIKETTY

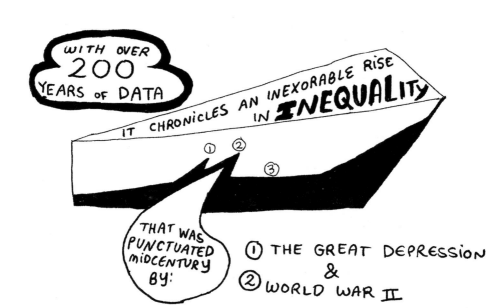

① THE GREAT DEPRESSION
&
② WORLD WAR II

FOLLOWED BY

③ 30 YEARS OF EVENLY-SPREAD PROSPERITY

THE KEYWORD THERE IS

COORDINATED

IF THIS ISSUE RE-EMERGES IN SAN FRANCISCO

(AND IT WILL)

YOU'D HAVE TO **MAKE SURE** THAT THE PROPOSED SOLUTIONS DON'T DRIVE AWAY

JOBS OR GROWTH-STAGE COMPANIES

THE PREVIOUS EMPLOYEE STOCK OPTIONS TAX WAS POORLY DESIGNED IN THE CONTEXT OF WHAT NEIGHBORING CITIES WERE DOING,

NOTHING ..WHICH WAS NOTHING

MOREOVER IT'S A HIGHLY VOLATILE

SOURCE OF TAX REVENUE

NO ONE HAD ANY IDEA THAT TWITTER'S IPO WOULD GO SO WELL

OR THAT ZYNGA'S WOULD GO SO TERRIBLY

YOU'D EITHER HAVE TO DESIGN

SOMETHING LESS PUNITIVE COMPARED TO NEIGHBORING CITIES

OR

SOMETHING THAT IS COORDINATED WITH THE REST OF SILICON VALLEY

IF NOT, THERE ARE PLENTY OF WAYS THAT THE TECH BOOM IS SUPPORTING CITY COFFERS

AT AN ANNUAL **$9.6 BILLION**

THE CITY'S CURRENT BUDGET IS **$3.2 BILLION** MORE

THAN WHAT IT WAS AT

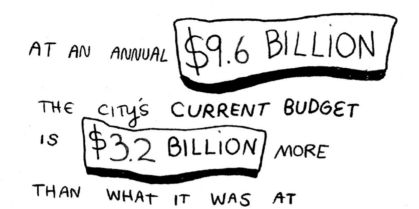

THE RECESSION'S LOW POINT

LARGELY BECAUSE OF THE

TECH FUELED

ECONOMIC RECOVERY

ALSO REMEMBER **PROP 13**

AND ALL THOSE HOUSES THAT ARE PAYING

TAXES TIED TO

1970's & 1980s

ASSESSMENTS?

WITH  A REVIVED REAL ESTATE MARKET

ALL OF THOSE HOMES ARE RE-ASSESSED AT CURRENT MARKET VALUES WHEN THEY GET SOLD.

SO THE CITY EXPECTED TO SEE $79 MILLION MORE IN PROPERTY TAXES THAN THE $1.15 BILLION IT HAD BUDGETED FOR FISCAL YEAR 2014.

AND AGAIN, WE'RE SWITCHING OVER TO

GROSS RECEIPTS

ANYWAY

ISN'T THE TECH COMMUNITY A BUNCH OF LIBERTARIANS WHO HAVE TOTAL DISREGARD FOR GOVERNMENT & TAXES?

NOT EXACTLY.

THIS GENERATION'S TECH LEADERSHIP

NO TAXES

DOESN'T HAVE A REFLEXIVE ANTI TAX ORIENTATION

LIKE THAT OF THE REAGAN ERA

THEY'RE NOT HAVING LAFFER CURVE PARTIES IN PRIVATE JETS TO BURNING MAN

IT'S MORE NUANCED.

SAM ALTMAN

PRESIDENT OF Y-COMBINATOR

"we could perhaps end poverty overnight"

HAS RUMINATED ON INCOME REDISTRIBUTION THROUGH A

UNIVERSAL BASIC INCOME

VENTURE CAPITALIST TIM DRAPER

WHO IS PUSHING A FAR-OUT PLAN TO BREAK CALIFORNIA INTO

6 SIX STATES

CONCEDED THAT SILICON VALLEY WOULD BE THE LEAST LIKELY TO SUPPORT IT OUT OF ALL THE HYPOTHETICAL CALIFORNIAS HE WANTS TO CREATE.

HE DIDN'T SAY WHY THOUGH

AND YOUR RENEGADE LAW-BREAKING
COMPANIES   AIR BnB & LYFT?

THEY PROVED PRODUCT-MARKET FIT

BUILT SOMETHING THAT PEOPLE WOULD PAY FOR

SCALED THEIR BUSINESSES

AND WERE TRANSFORMED & REINED INTO EXISTING REGULATORY + TAX INFRASTRUCTURE

AIRBnB REMITTED ITS 14% HOTEL TAX & SAW INCREASED ENFORCEMENT FROM THE CITY GOVERNMENT

WHICH MAKES THEM

"PRO-BUSINESS MODERATES"

IN SAN FRANCISCO TERMS.

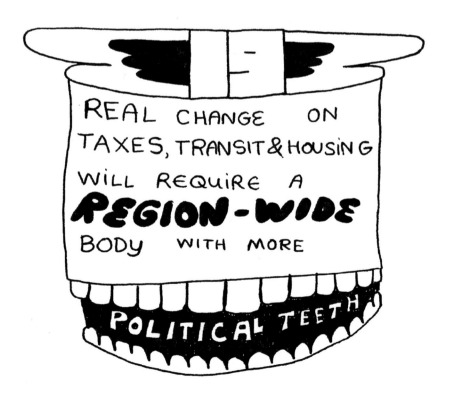

Progress Demands That the Bay Area Be De-Balkanized

FOR MORE THAN A CENTURY, THE BAY AREA'S

HOUSING, TRANSIT INFRASTRUCTURE & TAX SYSTEM

HAVE BEEN HAUNTED BY THE REGION'S

FRACTURED GOVERNANCE.

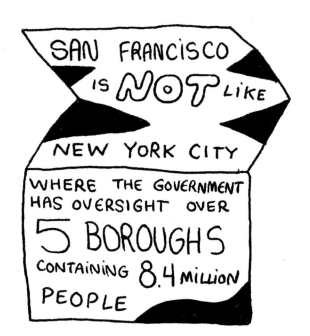

SAN FRANCISCO IS **NOT** LIKE

NEW YORK CITY

WHERE THE GOVERNMENT HAS OVERSIGHT OVER

5 BOROUGHS CONTAINING 8.4 MILLION PEOPLE

FOR THE 7 MILLION PEOPLE OF THE BAY AREA

IT'S EVERY CITY & COUNTY FOR THEMSELVES

WHILE THERE **IS** AN

Association of Bay Area Governments

"Serving the counties, cities and towns of the Bay Area since 1961"

ITS NOT SUFFICIENTLY **POWERFUL**

THAT MEANS NIMBYiSTS IN EVERY CITY TRY & SHOVE THE PROBLEM ONTO SOMEONE ELSE

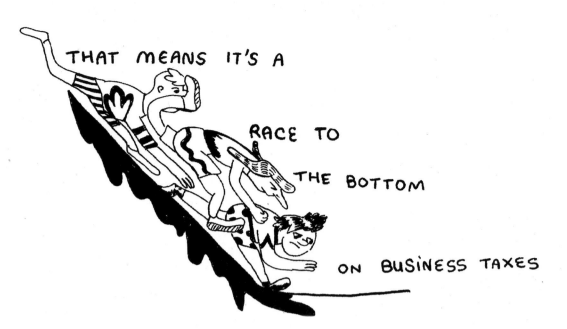

THAT MEANS IT'S A RACE TO THE BOTTOM ON BUSINESS TAXES

THAT MEANS THAT WE HAVE A

FRAGMENTED TRANSPORTATION SYSTEM (BETWEEN)

AND SO ON

BART <u>WOULD HAVE</u> RUN

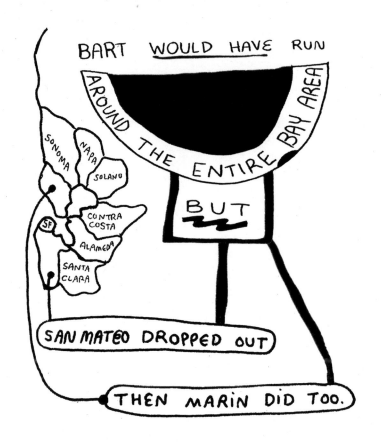

AROUND THE ENTIRE BAY AREA

BUT

SONOMA
NAPA
SOLANO
SF
CONTRA COSTA
ALAMEDA
SANTA CLARA

SAN MATEO DROPPED OUT

THEN MARIN DID TOO.

NOT ONLY IS

TRANSPORTATION

FRAGMENTED,

BUT SUBURBS HAVE BLOCKED MANY **DENSER** HOUSING

DEVELOPMENTS

ALONG CALTRAIN STATIONS

THAT WOULD HAVE SUPPORTED WORKFORCES FOR COMPANIES LIKE **GOOGLE & FACEBOOK**

CAL TRAIN

20

THIS IS OVERWHELMING. WHY DOESN'T GOOGLE JUST MOVE TO DETROIT?

ACTUALLY, THIS IS HAPPENING. JUST NOT IN DETROIT. YET.

DURING THE LAST  IT WAS HARD

TO THINK OF MORE THAN A

OF CITIES THAT BOASTED OF A

2014 STARTUP GENOME MAP

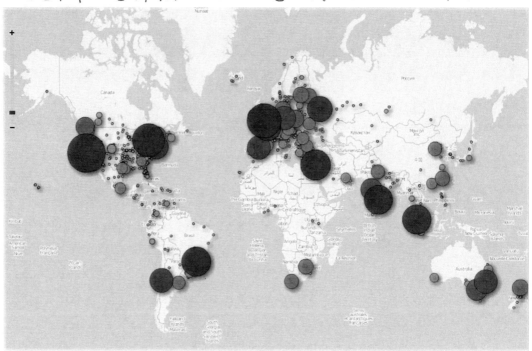

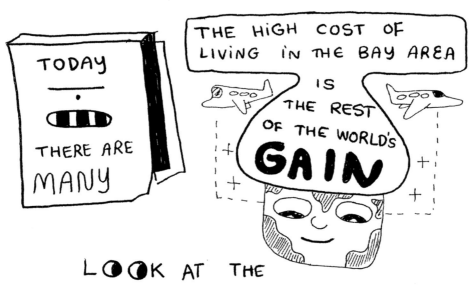

TODAY —• THERE ARE MANY

THE HIGH COST OF LIVING IN THE BAY AREA IS THE REST OF THE WORLD'S **GAIN**

LOOK AT THE THE NEIGHBORHOODS IN

SOUNDCLOUD // MITTE

KREUZBERG

OR

TSINGHUA UNIVERSITY

ZHONGGUANCUN

BERLIN

BEIJING
WHERE TSINGHUA UNIVERSITY IS SPROUTING COMPANIES.

IN

GREENPOINT

BROOKLYN

IN

ISRAEL

IN

N O I D A
OR
GURGAON

THE WORLD'S LEADING **BITCOIN** EXCHANGE CAME OUT OF **SLOVENIA**

THE WORLDS LEADING

& WAS JUST ACQUIRED FOR $2 BILLION BY FACEBOOK

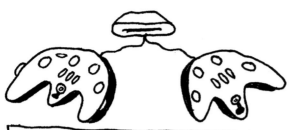

THE WORLD'S LEADING

MOBILE GAMING STARTUPS ARE IN HELSINKI + LONDON

THE WORLD'S MOST INTERESTING HANDSET MAKER, **XIAOMI** IS RUN OUT OF BEIJING.

4 YEARS AFTER LAUNCH, THEY EXPECT TO SHIP $11 BIL OF PRODUCTS

SNAPCHAT WAS STARTED BY A HANDFUL OF STANFORD GRADUATES WHO COULD HAVE STAYED HERE A DECADE AGO

BUT ITS RUN OUT OF A BEACH HOUSE IN VENICE

OK, MAKE FUN OF THEM

JUST DECAMPED FOR LOS ANGELES BECAUSE WAREHOUSE SPACE WAS TOO EXPENSIVE IN THE BAY AREA.

SILICON VALLEY IS STILL THE DENSEST & STRONGEST TECH ECOSYSTEM IN THE WORLD

BUT ITS ONLY AHEAD BECAUSE -

IN STARTUP PARLANCE

IT'S A "FIRST MOVER"

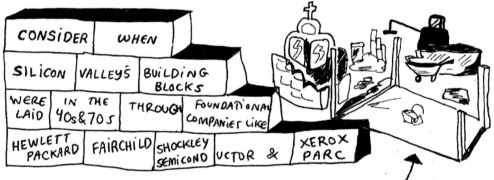

CONSIDER WHEN SILICON VALLEY'S BUILDING BLOCKS WERE LAID IN THE 40s & 70s THROUGH FOUNDATIONAL COMPANIES LIKE HEWLETT PACKARD, FAIRCHILD, SHOCKLEY SEMICOND UCTOR & XEROX PARC

AT THAT TIME, THE REST OF THE WORLD'S MAJOR ECONOMIES WERE BEING REBUILT.

POST-WWII

EUROPE WAS RECONSTRUCTING

AND INDIA & CHINA WERE JUST ESTABLISHING NATIONAL UNITY & SYSTEMS OF GOVERNANCE

BOTH INDIA & CHINA HAVE MADE **MAJOR** ECONOMIC **REFORMS** SINCE THEN

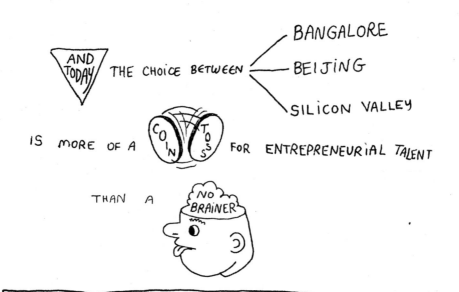

AND TODAY THE CHOICE BETWEEN
- BANGALORE
- BEIJING
- SILICON VALLEY

IS MORE OF A *COIN TOSS* FOR ENTREPRENEURIAL TALENT

THAN A *NO BRAINER*

WHILE SILICON VALLEY CERTAINLY ISN'T IN PERIL

IT'S CONTINUED RESILIENCE DEPENDS ON WHETHER IT CAN KEEP ATTRACTING

THE BEST TALENT & NEW IDEAS

FROM EVERYWHERE

21. WE'RE FUCKED.

NO, WE'RE NOT FUCKED.

IF YOU'VE READ THIS FAR,

YOU KNOW WHY WE'RE HERE

WE'RE PAYING CRAZY RENTS

OR &

ROLLING AROUND GMUNI BALLS IN THE STREETS

BECAUSE THE BAY AREA HAD DONE A LOT OF THINGS RIGHT.

I KNOW THAT A BROOKINGS STUDY SHOWING THAT:

SAN FRANCISCO HAD THE **LARGEST INCREASES** IN INCOME INEQUALITY

IS DISTRESSING

BUT DO YOU KNOW WHAT ELSE IS TRUE?

SAN FRANCISCO & SAN JOSE HAVE THE HIGHEST LEVELS OF INCOME MOBILITY

IN THE COUNTRY

HARVARD + BERKELEY ECONOMISTS RAJ CHETTY, NATHANIEL HENDREN PATRICK KLINE & EMMANUEL SAEZ

EXAMINED FEDERAL INCOME TAX RECORDS FOR 40 MILLION CHILDREN & THEIR PARENTS

BETWEEN 1996 - 2012

THEY FOUND THAT CHILDREN IN SAN JOSE & SAN FRANCISCO

HAD THE HIGHEST CHANCES OF MOVING FROM THE BOTTOM INCOME QUINTILE

TO THE TOP INCOME QUINTILE OUT OF ALL MAJOR METROPOLITAN AREAS IN THE UNITED STATES

THERE ARE ABSURD STORIES, LIKE THAT OF THE WHATSAPP FOUNDER WHO WENT FROM FOOD STAMPS TO SELLING A MESSAGING APP TO FACEBOOK FOR $19 BILLION

JAN KOUM

THEN THERE ARE MORE REALISTIC STORIES

LIKE THAT OF MY MOTHER

SHE MOVED HERE IN THE LATE 1970s AS A VIETNAMESE REFUGEE

BECAUSE MY GRANDPARENTS WERE TOO OLD TO WORK & THEY COULDN'T SPEAK ENGLISH,

MY MOTHER & HER FIVE SISTERS  THEIR EARNINGS

& COLLECTIVELY BOUGHT

 A HOME IN SAN JOSE

ALL WHILE STILL IN THEIR MID-20's

WE HAVE TO REMEMBER THAT CITIES ARE UNEQUAL BECAUSE

THE OPPORTUNITIES THEY PROVIDE ATTRACT

BOTH

THE VERY RICH & THE VERY POOR

SAN FRANCISCO'S **EXTREME** JUXTAPOSITIONS OF WEALTH & POVERTY EXIST BECAUSE THE CITY IS BOTH AN EXTREMELY DESIRABLE PLACE TO LIVE **AND** IT MAINTAINS PROTECTIONS FOR ITS RESIDENTS THROUGH PROGRAMS LIKE

RENT CONTROL

AND $165 MILLION/YR IN SPENDING ON HOMELESSNESS

THE GLEAMING, ONYX NEMA TOWERS EXIST SIDE-BY-SIDE HOMELESSNESS BECAUSE SAN FRANCISCO CREATED THE MID-MARKET PROGRAM TO LURE COMPANIES LIKE TWITTER

AND BECAUSE THE

SINGLE-ROOM OCCUPANCY HOTELS & NONPROFITS

THAT HOUSE & FEED THE CITY'S POOREST RESIDENTS HAVE BEEN POLITICALLY PROTECTED FOR DECADES.

BOTH THE TECH INDUSTRY & SAN FRANCISCO HAVE DELICATE ECOLOGIES THAT HAVE TAKEN DECADES TO CULTIVATE.

AS THEY BECOME MORE INTERTWINED

THE POLITICAL WINDS OF THE CITY

ARE SHIFTING.

THEY CAN GO IN EITHER

AN INCREASINGLY ANTAGONISTIC DIRECTION

OR A NEW CONSENSUS COULD EMERGE

WHETHER THAT MEANS

 SIGNING A PETITION FOR ELLIS ACT REFORM

CALLING OR E-MAILING EVICTING ENTITIES

ENTERING PUBLIC COMMENT IN FAVOR OF DENSITY BONUSES

OR BOYCOTTING ELLIS ACT EVICTION PROPERTIES

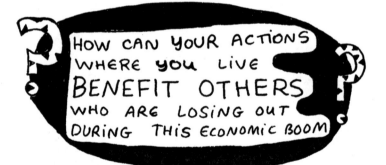

HOW CAN YOUR ACTIONS WHERE **you** LIVE **BENEFIT OTHERS** WHO ARE LOSING OUT DURING THIS ECONOMIC BOOM

HOW WILL YOU PARTICIPATE IN YOUR COMMUNITY?

CHARITY? VOLUNTEERING? TAXES?

HOMEOWNERS IN NEIGHBORHOOD ASSOCIATIONS & IN THE PENINSULA:

MINE

THE TECH INDUSTRY IS HELPING YOUR HOME VALUES SKYROCKET

BUT YOUR PROPERTY TAXES HAVE NOT KEPT UP WITH THE COST OF PROVIDING SERVICES OR SCHOOLS.

CLOSED
OUT OF
SCHOOL

STOP SITTING IN THE BACKGROUND WHILE THE CITY'S POOR, WORKING-CLASS, ELDERLY & YOUNG DUKE IT OUT

IN THIS **UGLY CHARADE**

OH DEAR

WHILE THERE ARE SOME TECH WORKERS WHO

STRIKE IT RICH,

MOST JUST HAVE A SALARY & WOULD LOVE TO RAISE FAMILIES IN THE BAY AREA JUST LIKE YOU A FEW YEARS AGO

THE BAY AREA RISKS BECOMING "A VICTIM OF ITS OWN SUCCESS"

IF IT CAN'T MAKE **MORE ROOM.**

AT THIS POINT

BLOCKING INDEPENDENT HOUSING DEVELOPMENTS TO PROTECT YOUR VIEWS IS TANTAMOUNT TO

GENERATIONAL THEFT.

ACTIVISTS

• • •

INVOKING CEQA CLAUSES TO STALL THE CITY'S TECH SHUTTLE PROGRAM SO THAT 1,400 OF 4,000 TECH BUS RIDERS MAY OR MAY NOT MOVE SLIGHTLY SOUTH

IS NOT A GAME-CHANGING WAY TO ADDRESS HOUSING AFFORDABILITY IN S.F.

THE INDUSTRY'S LEADERSHIP IS ASKING FOR ELLIS ACT REFORM TO BE BACKED BY TECH COMPANIES.

BUT WITHOUT <u>SERIOUS ADDITIONS</u> TO THE <u>ENTIRE REGION'S</u> HOUSING SUPPLY, THESE CRISIS MEASURES JUST MAKE

SAN FRANCISCO'S EXISTING MIDDLE & WORKING-CLASS A HIGHLY-PROTECTED BUT ENDANGERED SPECIES

IN THE LONG RUN

WITH SUCH <u>LIMITED</u> RENTAL STOCK AVAILABLE ON THE MARKET AT ANY GIVEN TIME

WHAT KIND OF PERSON CAN AFFORD TO MOVE HERE TODAY WITH A MEDIAN RENT OF

$3,350?

FOR THE MORE EXTREME GROUPS:

YOU CANNOT LOGICALLY FIGHT BOTH DEVELOPMENT & DISPLACEMENT

THE REAL ESTATE SPECULATION RUNNING THROUGH THE CITY RIGHT NOW IS JUST AS MUCH

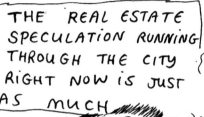

A BET ON POLITICAL PARALYSIS IN THE FACE OF A LONG-TERM HOUSING SHORTAGE

AS IT IS ON SAN FRANCISCO'S *DESIRABILITY* AS A PLACE TO LIVE.

FURTHERMORE

THE ANTAGONISM ONLY ENSURES THAT

THIEVES ARE YE!

DEALS WILL HAPPEN BEHIND CLOSED DOORS.

FOR THE MORE PRAGMATIC GROUPS:

THE TECH COMMUNITY COULD EASILY BE CONVINCED TO SUPPORT INCLUSIONARY HOUSING, PROVIDED THE NUMBERS STILL WORK OUT FOR DEVELOPERS

AND THAT LOTS MORE HOUSING GETS BUILT

IN CONCLUSION

THE CRISIS WE ARE SEEING IS THE RESULT OF

DECADES OF

CHOICES

AND WHILE THE TECH INDUSTRY IS A **SEXY** ATTENTION-GRABBING

TARGET

IT CANNOT SHOULDER BLAME FOR THIS ALONE.

IF THIS CONTINUES, THINGS WILL KEEP GETTING WORSE UNTIL THE NEXT ECONOMIC CRASH, AND WILL RE-SURFACE AGAIN

OR IT WILL KEEP SPILLING OVER INTO OAKLAND, WHICH IS A WHOLE OTHER

PANDORA'S BOX OF—GENTRIFICATION ISSUES

HIGH HOUSING COSTS AREN'T HEALTHY FOR THE CITY

NOR ARE THEY HEALTHY FOR THE INDUSTRY.

BOTH THRIVE ON A CONSTANT FLOW OF NEW IDEAS AND PEOPLE.

SO WHILE GOOGLE MIGHT NOT BE OPENING A GIANT OFFICE IN DETROIT ANYTIME SOON

THE PEOPLE OF DETROIT & THE MIDWEST ARE COMING HERE.

I MEET THEM EVERYDAY.

THERE ARE PEOPLE LIKE

BRIAN CLARK

WHO ACTUALLY MOVED FROM DETROIT & WAS LIVING OFF VARIOUS HACKATHON WINNINGS WHILE TEACHING CODING IN MISSIONBITS AFTERSCHOOL PROGRAM.

HE WAS SLEEPING ON FRIENDS' COUCHES & EATING ONE MEAL A DAY

UNTIL HE WON THE LAUNCH HACKATHON & GOT INITIAL FUNDING FOR A NEW STARTUP CALLED VUE, A MOBILE FEEDBACK & USER ENGAGEMENT TOOL HE BUILT.

OR LIKE **REY FAUSTINO** WHO GREW UP IN A WORKING CLASS FAMILY IN SOUTHERN CALIFORNIA THAT RELIED ON SOCIAL SERVICES & FOOD STAMPS TO MAKE ENDS MEET.

NOW HE IS WORKING ON FIXING THE PROBLEMS HE REMEMBERED AS A CHILD THROUGH ONE DEGREE, A YELP-LIKE APP THAT HELPS BAY AREA FAMILIES FIND THE RIGHT NON-PROFITS & SOCIAL SERVICES FOR THEM.

IT'S SUPPORTED BY Y-COMBINATOR & HAS THOUSANDS OF USERS.

MANY OF THE PEOPLE WHO COME HERE **WILL STAY**

AND MAKE VITAL CONTRIBUTIONS FOR DECADES THROUGH THEIR WORK

THEIR TAXES

& THEIR CHARITABLE CONTRIBUTIONS.

SOME WILL COME FOR A WHILE

& THEN GO BACK & INVIGORATE ENTREPRENEURIAL ECOSYSTEMS **BACK HOME.**

THIS CIRCULATION OF CREATIVE TALENT IS **CRUCIAL** FOR THE BAY AREA & THE REST OF THE U.S.

AFTERWORD

As I'm sure you're now aware, land use in California is a complicated beast. Three years after writing the initial essay, there are five issues I think deserve more attention in understanding how we got here:

Federal housing subsidies in America are deeply regressive.

One point of view I sometimes run into among more affluent residents of San Francisco is a complaint that the city spends way too much on homelessness. The city's Department of Homelessness and Supportive Housing has a budget of $242 million.[1] A common misperception and calculation, given that the last Point-in-Time Count recorded 6,686 people experiencing homelessness,[2] is that the city must be spending $36,000 per homeless person. However, half of this $242 million is spent on roughly 6,000 supportive housing units that house people who would otherwise be homeless. Less than $40 million is spent on shelters.[3]

On top of that, what people don't realize is that the federal government subsidizes housing, primarily to upper-middle-class property owners, while cities largely carry the burden of funding solutions to homelessness on their own.

One of the largest tax deductions is the mortgage-interest deduction, which comes in at $77 billion per year.[4] Because California is so populous and because its housing is so expensive, about one-fifth of the tax benefits of that deduction go toward property owners in this state.[5] But this tax benefit doesn't actually increase the homeownership rate in supply restricted markets, according to a Federal Reserve Bank study from the St. Louis branch.[6] In constrained housing markets like coastal California, the deduction just gets priced into the cost of housing, making each unit—and the land underlying it—more expensive than it would otherwise be. If one were to do a back-of-the-envelope calculation on federal tax savings on a $1 million mortgage,[7] it would be close to $20,000 a year from that deduction alone, which is more than what the city spends on average on a person experiencing homelessness.

On top of that benefit is the non-taxation of imputed rent, which brings the U.S.'s total tax benefits to homeowners to around $600 billion, according to the University of Pennsylvania's Todd Sinai and Joseph Gyourko.[8] Landlords must pay taxes on their rental income from tenants in addition to property taxes, but homeowners don't pay tax on their effective rental costs. This isn't an argument for taxing imputed rent; it's just pointing out another structural imbalance between the way that tenants and homeowners are treated by U.S. tax law.

Compared to all of this, the U.S. government only spends $46 billion a year on means-tested housing programs and low-income housing tax credits.[9] Housing support for low-income Americans has fallen so far behind since the early 1980s that federal rental vouchers only cover one out of every four low-income families who qualify for them, according to Evicted: Poverty and Profit in the American City,[10] the Pulitzer-prize winning book from Harvard University sociologist Matthew Desmond.

All of this has led to a system that shifts more and more wealth toward property owners amid a generation and a half of broad-based wage stagnation in the U.S. In a widely read critique of Thomas Piketty's opus on inequality, MIT graduate Matthew Rognlie pointed out that housing is responsible for almost all increases in returns on capital versus non-housing wealth.[11]

Prop. 13 distorts land markets and is also deeply regressive.

In the original piece, I talked about the twin histories of rent control and Proposition 13's property tax caps and how they came into existence between 1978 and 1979.

But I think I could have discussed more deeply how Proposition 13 completely distorts land markets in California. In California, because property taxes are capped at whatever price a person or company bought a piece of property at and can increase by no more than two percent a year, we effectively award all returns on land to whoever owned property first.

This is different from other states in the U.S., and it leads to wildly different tax assessments for similar kinds of housing depending on when a person bought in. A person who bought a house in the 1970s might be paying less than a thousand dollars a year in property tax, while their neighbor who bought in at $1.5 million might be paying 15 times as much.

Not only that, these low tax assessments are transferrable to children and grandchildren in what political journalist Peter Schrag called a "dynasty provision" in his book Paradise Lost: California's Experience, America's Future.[12] (Californians also abolished the state inheritance tax a few years after

Proposition 13 in 1982.) In his dissent to Proposition 13 a decade after that, Supreme Court Justice John Paul Stevens would only refer to the beneficiaries of the law as "Squires" with a capital 'S,' as a play on the law's feudalistic character.[13]

Proposition 13 incentivizes land-banking, which was especially common in Oakland after the foreclosure crisis.[14] Speculators will come in and purchase property, holding it to ride the price appreciation while keeping it vacant. The state's Legislative Analyst's Office found that the likelihood a property gets developed falls to almost zero if it has been held for longer than ten years.[15] Land brokers go around and egg parcel owners to sell their land at only the very highest prices, which constrains a developer's ability to sell finished product or housing units that are accessible to buyers at anything but the highest incomes.

Like the mortgage interest deduction, Proposition 13 is regressive, because wealthier individuals tend to own homes while low-income residents can't afford to buy property. The Legislative Analyst's Office found that two-thirds of Proposition 13's tax relief goes to those with incomes higher than $80,000, with the bulk of that relief going to homeowners with incomes in excess of $120,000. (California's median household income is $61,818.)[16]

It also distorts municipal finance among California cities. Property tax is one of the most stable and reliable forms of public revenue. Without it, the state of California has become more dependent on income tax, which is progressive but unpredictable.[17] Likewise, cities have come to rely on fees to sustain basic infrastructure[18] because they don't have a sufficient, built-in revenue source.

When the Legislative Analyst's Office surveyed states with impact fees, they found that California had the highest average fees for construction of a single-family home and that they were almost three times as high as the average across all states with fees.[19] San Francisco's fees, in particular, are the highest in the country at $72,000 per unit, according to The Wall Street Journal.[20]

This creates an overall dynamic where existing property owners get to capture virtually all of the gains on their land appreciation, while the cost of affordable housing and services instead gets baked into the cost of new housing units through fees. This dynamic most visibly plays out in fights over inclusionary housing, or what percentage of units developers should be compelled to build that are below-market-rate by law.

In the context of Proposition 13 and the regressive federal housing system, inclusionary housing basically protects the property values of existing homeowners, while pressuring developers for a token number of below-market-rate units. San Francisco has averaged 1,891 units a year over the past two decades,[21] while the city's inclusionary program has created around 306 units a year, or 4,600 of permanently affordable housing units since 2002.[22] This was happening as the city was adding 10,000 people per year[23] and as the median property value rose by $450,000 between 2010 and 2016.[24]

On a year of strong appreciation, the value of all residential real estate rises substantially. In 2015, the market value of all housing in San Francisco appreciated by $131 billion.[25] In contrast, the city's voters have only passed two affordable housing bonds in the last 20 years, worth $410 million.

To be clear, the inclusionary program is vital in the context of declining state and federal support for low-income housing. But its benefits are often overstated in highly politicized negotiations over the requirements, as the program only accounts for producing about ten percent of the city's below market rate units. If inclusionary percentages are pushed too high, they make new development infeasible and effectively channel even more wealth to existing homeowners and landlords.

Ultimately, the fight underscores the fundamental contradiction of American housing policy[26]—in that we want housing to both be a good investment and we want it to remain broadly affordable—which is impossible.

California cities are incentivized by the state's tax system to reject housing and add jobs.

The Proposition 13 discussion leads to the other destructive dynamic of California's taxation system, which is that cities love to add jobs and commercial real estate, which generates tax revenue, and hate to add housing, which is often a money-loser or barely break even on new tax revenue against the cost of providing services like schools, fire and police.

In San Jose, which has long had a precarious fiscal structure since Proposition 13 passed in 1978, employment lands take up only 15 percent of the city's total land area but contribute a net $124 million to the city's budget.[27] In contrast, all residential lands—which make up 57 percent of the city's area, have a net negative impact of $110 million on the city's budget. Most of the negative impact is from older single-family homes, which have not been sold or re-assessed in recent years.

You can see this dynamic play out in cities like Brisbane, which is just south of San Francisco and is considering whether to add hotel, office or housing units to a 684-acre parcel.[28] If the city added a hotel, five million square feet of office and no housing, it would see $8.6 million more in net tax revenue a year.[29] But if the city added 4,434 housing units, six million square feet of office space and a smaller amount of hotel zoning, it would see only $1.1 million in extra tax revenue and it would have to culturally absorb more than twice as many residents as it currently has.

Across all 101 cities and nine counties of the Bay Area region, this creates a situation where everyone wants the office jobs and the ensuing tax revenue, but no one wants to house or take care of the people who come with that space. Cities are incentivized to do so in part because they are facing enormous structural issues in unfunded pension liabilities. Even though Proposition 13 was meant to be an anti-tax initiative, it had the perverse effect of consolidating power at the state level away from municipalities. This made it easier for public sector unions to negotiate benefits without the long-term costs being fully transparent to voters.[30]

Given that people are living longer and that historically low interest rates are contributing to lower-than-expected returns, public pensions themselves are seeing serious structural imbalances.[31] In 2014, the unfunded liability of California's 130 state and local government pension plans stood at $241.3 billion,[32] according to the state's controller office. On top of that are $125 billion in unfunded retiree healthcare costs, creating a total debt of $366 billion.[33]

California can't renege on its promises to public sector workers, especially because of the way the state court system has historically interpreted these contracts.[34] So the additional costs of servicing these pensions must come out of current city budgets, which eats into services offered to current and future residents. On top of housing, these pension liabilities represent yet another generational wealth transfer from the young to the old and from future Californians to retirees.

This is why San Francisco's city contributions into the retirement system increased by 66,733 *percent* between 2000 and 2010,[35] and is partially why the city is expected to face an $848 million deficit over the next five years.[36] Ultimately, these deficits are why cities like San Francisco and Oakland are so eager to attract technology employers to boost tax revenue, even though a disproportionate share of that economic growth is just absorbed by landlords and property owners under Proposition 13 and even though this creates serious displacement risks for low-income residents and tenants.

While less fiscally stable cities like Oakland and San Jose try to attract companies, affluent suburbs like Palo Alto and Menlo Park hoard revenue through local property and sales tax from the bigger technology companies like Google, Facebook, Apple and Palantir, but export their workers—and the cost of servicing them—elsewhere by not building housing.

Cupertino, for example, is home to the world's most valuable company, Apple, which has a market capitalization of $754 billion and has a cash pile of $250 billion largely stored abroad.[37] But Cupertino only houses ten percent of the company's local workforce,[38] and is only required by the state's Regional Housing Needs Assessment to build 1,064 units by 2022,[39] even though it allowed Apple to open a 12,000-person campus this spring.[40] (The suburb's median home value is $1.8 million.)

A handful of tech companies are now the most valuable companies in the world, and this entails more scrutiny and public responsibility.

One other shift that has happened since I published the story three years ago, is that the top five most valuable companies in the world by market capitalization today are all technology companies.[41] Three of them are in the Bay Area, and two of them are in Seattle—both metros with serious housing affordability crises. This wasn't the case a few years ago, when tech companies were powerful but had not yet displaced oil companies and Berkshire Hathaway as the most valuable in the world.

The big five tech companies—Apple, Alphabet, Microsoft, Amazon and Facebook—are responsible for most of the value creation in the technology industry over the last decade. They've grown from roughly $500 billion in collective market capitalization a decade ago to $2.7 trillion today. In comparison, all of the "unicorns" or privately-held companies worth more than $1 billion are valued at $660 billion in total.

This newfound power and wealth means big tech deserves substantially more scrutiny and pressure. Yet in the public discourse, there's a lot of confusion over who has power over what.

California cities are highly restricted by decades of anti-tax, anti-government ballot initiatives passed by previous generations of voters. Any new, revenue-generating tax must be passed by a two-thirds, super-majority of voters, according to 1996's Proposition 218.[42] As such, it can takes months or years of planning and marketing to pass a ballot initiative that raises taxes or passes a bond and a minority of voters can kill any effort.

On top of that, repatriation of overseas capital is a federal corporate tax reform issue, not one that local municipalities or that the state of California has control over. At 35 percent, the U.S. has one of the highest listed corporate tax rates in the OECD. But its effective rates are much lower, at around 25 percent, because of numerous deductions, loopholes and credits.[43] Companies like Apple keep hundreds of billions of dollars abroad, in part, because the U.S. is one of the few countries that taxes income earned globally, as opposed to income earned only domestically.[44] Corporate tax reform and repatriation is currently in play under the Trump administration, with a proposed corporate tax cut to 15 percent on passthroughs and LLCs, which will make the American tax system more regressive. But given the GOP's inability to successfully vote on any changes to healthcare law, it's unclear how politically feasible tax reform can be.

In reality, most of the wealth of the Silicon Valley is captured at the California state level—not the city or regional level—through income and capital gains taxation. After Proposition 13, the state came to rely more and more on personal income taxes, which make up 70 percent of the state's General Fund and are projected to come in at $91 billion this year.[45] The top one percent of the state's earners, who take home one-fourth of the state's income, are responsible for 48 percent of those state income tax proceeds.[46] The Bay Area, which makes up 16.9 percent of the California's population, is responsible for 37 percent of its income tax revenue.[47]

But unlike New York, California cities can't levy their own municipal income taxes. While some local legislators like supervisor Aaron Peskin have tried to push a resolution around this,[48] it's unlikely that the state legislature or governor Jerry Brown would pass this and give up their own power considering California's own highly unstable revenue system. The dependence on a small number of earners and on capital gains revenue[49] effectively ties the state of California to the performance of U.S. equity markets, which whiplashes the state government between abundance and austerity.

In the last recession, the state faced a $40 billion shortfall, but the current rainy day fund is only slated to have $7.9 billion in it by the end of the fiscal year.[50] Alan Auerbach, a UC Berkeley economist who served on a state council examining tax reform, found that California's system is 50 percent more volatile than New York's and three times as volatile as Texas' system.[51]

In the study Auerbach was a part of, a final report discussed reforms ranging from a wealth tax, to income averaging for capital gains revenue over several years, to a broad-based VAT or services tax that would cover the software industry, among many other options.[52]

If a regional push for revenue were ever created, it would need to fix the way that big tech, like Apple, spreads it workers over dozens of cities, but pays most of its local tax revenue into only its headquarters city. A smart policy would also distinguish between big, publicly-traded technology companies that operate quasi-monopolies over e-commerce or online advertising versus startups that have only recently found product-market fit and are barely profitable.

However, absent comprehensive tax reform in California, the state's cities are stuck in a race-to-the-bottom with each other on business taxes and fees, or rely on one-off negotiations for community benefits when new campuses or headquarters are built. Meanwhile, affluent Bay Area workers keep the California state budget afloat through their income and capital gains taxes.

Corporations and wealthy individuals have engaged in some philanthropy and their giving as a percentage of income is growing faster than the rest of California and the U.S.,[53] but it is relatively small compared to the need. Since 2009, the amount that Silicon Valley companies have given away locally has grown from $56 million to $117 million in 2015, according to Open Impact, a Bay Area firm that provides strategic advisory on philanthropy and social change.[54]

The amount of capital parked in donor-advised funds has also grown to $7.3 billion for Silicon Valley Community Foundation and then $2.2 billion for Fidelity Charitable and Schwab Charitable locally in the Bay Area.[55] These funds deployed $75.4 million in grants toward Santa Clara and San Mateo county nonprofits in 2015. But again, unlike foundations, donor-advised funds are not obligated to set aside any certain percentage of capital every year and philanthropy is inherently less transparent and democratically accountable.

We must continue monitoring overseas capital into local housing markets.

Overseas capital is often used as a red herring to block new market-rate construction.[56] But throughout the most recent boom, some of the highest-grossing realtor firms have actually been on the peninsula,[57] where little new housing has been built at all and where existing suburban tract homes are traded, refurbished with high-end interiors and then sold.

Given federal tax subsidies, state property tax caps and highly restrictive zoning laws, coastal California real estate has become an exceptionally protected asset to park capital in, regardless of whether it comes in the form of a newly constructed condo or a 100-year-old Victorian.

Detached single-family homes are perhaps the most attractive place to park capital in, because there will never be a meaningful number of them ever built again on the California coast. Between 1998 and 2015, the median Palo Alto home appreciated at more than four times the rate that the S&P 500 increased. Limited liability corporations are used to mask multiple buyers of mid-Peninsula suburban homes.[58]

Because countries like the U.S. and the U.K. emphasize property and real estate as an investable asset while having restrictive land-use regimes, that makes their housing an attractive place to store capital even if units are not used as shelter. Supply restrictions even amplify shocks from foreign capital flows into local housing markets.[59]

Many other countries have studied and restricted the effect of these flows. The Canadian city of Vancouver, for example, put a 15 percent property tax on foreign home buyers,[60] while Switzerland maintains a quota on the number of residential properties that can be sold to foreigners. Australia encourages foreign investment into new residential construction, but controls it on the purchase of existing housing units.[61]

Then under the Obama Administration, the Department of Justice began investigating secret buyers of luxury real estate.[62] But it's doubtful that this will continue under Donald Trump, a real estate developer who benefits from these flows, and his Attorney General Jeff Sessions.

I've yet to see a major American city really study or address this issue. SPUR did a small study, finding that only 2.4 percent of San Francisco's housing stock are vacant, non-primary residences.[63] But Zillow found that about one-third of the overseas Chinese shoppers[64] it tracks focus on six U.S. markets including San Jose and San Francisco. They tend to compete with more affluent buyers for homes, and shop for higher-end homes. This issue may have to wait until another administration, unfortunately.

WORKS CITED

Foreword

1. "Workforce Housing." Bay Area Council. N.p., n.d. Web. 18 May 2017.
2. Dillon, Liam. "More than 130 Bills Take Aim at California's Housing Crisis." Los Angeles Times. Los Angeles Times, 20 Mar. 2017. Web. 18 May 2017.

Afterword

1. Department of Homelessness and Supportive Housing. N.p., n.d. Web. 18 May 2017.
2. Green, Samantha. Homeless Point-In-Time Count & Survey Comprehensive Report 2015. Rep. Comp. Peter Connery. San Francisco: Applied Survey Research, 2015. Print.
3. "Historic Spending on Homeless Services in San Francisco." Department of Homelessness and Supportive Housing. Department of Homelessness and Supportive Housing, n.d. Web. 18 May 2017.
4. DeSilver, Drew. "The Biggest U.S. Tax Breaks." Pew Research Center. N.p., 06 Apr. 2016. Web. 18 May 2017.
5. Sinai, Todd, and Joseph Gyourko. The (Un)changing Geographical Distribution of Housing Tax Benefits: 1980 to 2000. University of Pennsylvania, 20 Nov. 2003. Web. 18 May 2017.
6. Sommer, Kamila, and Paul Sullivan. Implications of U.S. Tax Policy for House Prices and Rents. Rep. St Louis Federal Reserve, Feb. 2012. Web. 18 May 2017.
7. "Mortgage Tax Deduction Calculator." Mortgage Interest Tax Deduction Calculator - Bankrate. Bankrate, n.d. Web. 18 May 2017.
8. Sinai, Todd, and Joseph Gyourko. The (Un)changing Geographical Distribution of Housing Tax Benefits: 1980 to 2000. University of Pennsylvania, 20 Nov. 2003. Web. 18 May 2017.
9. Collinson, Robert A.; Ellen, Ingrid Gould; and Ludwig, Jens, "Low-Income Housing Policy" (2015). Kreisman Working Paper Series in Housing Law and Policy. Paper 34.http://chicagounbound.uchicago.edu/ housing_law_and_policy/34
10. Desmond, Matthew. Evicted: Poverty and Profit in the American City. London: Penguin, 2017. Print.
11. "NIMBYs in the Twenty-first Century." The Economist. The Economist Newspaper, 25 Mar. 2015. Web. 18 May 2017.

12. Schrag, Peter. Paradise Lost: California's Experience, America's Future: Updated with a New Preface. Berkeley: U of California, 2004. Print.

13. Greenhouse, Linda. "Justices Affirm Law in California Restricting Property Tax Increases." The New York Times. The New York Times, 18 June 1992. Web. 18 May 2017.

14. Cagle, Susie. "The Oakland Raiders." The New Inquiry. N.p., 18 Apr. 2017. Web. 18 May 2017.

15. Taylor, Mac. "Common Claims About Proposition 13." Legislative Analysts' Office of California. N.p., Sept. 2016. Web. 18 May 2017.

16. "Population Estimates, July 1, 2016, (V2016)." California QuickFacts from the US Census Bureau. N.p., n.d. Web. 18 May 2017.

17. State of California Office of the Controller. "Comprehensive Tax Reform in California: A Contextual Framework." California State Controller Betty T. Yee & the Controller's Council of Economic Advisors on Tax Reform, June 2016. Web. 18 May 2017.

18. Ibid.

19. Taylor, Mac. "Common Claims About Proposition 13." Legislative Analysts' Office of California. N.p., Sept. 2016. Web. 18 May 2017.

20. Timiraos, Nick. "How City Hall Exacerbates the Entry-Level Housing Squeeze." The Wall Street Journal. Dow Jones & Company, 05 May 2016. Web. 18 May 2017.

21. 2015 San Francisco Housing Inventory. Rep. San Francisco Planning Department, Apr. 2015. Web. May 2017.

22. "Planning Code Text Amendments Inclusionary Affordable Housing Program." San Francisco Planning Department, 27 Apr. 2017. Web. 19 May 2017.

23. "Population Estimates, July 1, 2016, (V2016)." San Francisco County California QuickFacts from the US Census Bureau. U.S. Census, n.d. Web. 18 May 2017.

24. Zillow, Inc. "San Francisco CA Home Prices & Home Values." Zillow. N.p., n.d. Web. 18 May 2017.

25. McDermid, Riley. "San Francisco Home Values Soared $131 Billion in 2015." Bizjournals.com. San Francisco Business Times, 4 Jan. 2016. Web. 18 May 2017.

26. Hertz, Daniel. "Housing Can't Be a Good Investment and Affordable." City Observatory. N.p., 20 July 2016. Web. 18 May 2017.

27. Szambelan, Sarah Jo, Egon Terplan, and Bob Brownstein. Back in the Black A Fiscal Strategy for Investing in San Jose's Future. Rep. San Jose: SPUR, 2016. Www.spur.org/sjfiscalstrategy. SPUR. Web. 19 May 2017.

28. Preliminary Assessment of Fiscal Impacts Brisbane Baylands, Brisbane California. Rep. Keyser Marston Associates, Inc., Mar. 2016. Web. 18 May 2017.

29. Ibid.

30. Mathews, Joe, and Mark Paul. California Crackup: How Reform Broke the Golden State and How We Can Fix It. Berkeley: U of California, 2010. Print.

31. Walsh, Mary Williams. "Calpers Cuts Investment Targets, Increasing Strain on Municipalities." The New York Times. The New York Times, 21 Dec. 2016. Web. 18 May 2017.

32. "Defined Benefit Systems - 12-year UAAL Trend | Open Data." Socrata. California State Controller's Office, n.d. Web. 18 May 2017.

33. Lin, Judy. "Understanding California's Public Pension Debt." Los Angeles Times. Los Angeles Times, 18 Sept. 2016. Web. 18 May 2017.

34. Monahan, Amy, Statutes as Contracts? The 'California Rule' and its Impact on Public Pension Reform (September 26, 2011). Iowa Law Review, Vol. 97, 2012; Minnesota Legal Studies Research Paper No. 11-40. Available at SSRN: https://ssrn.com/abstract=1933887 or http://dx.doi.org/10.2139/ssrn.1933887

35. Wachs, Benjamin. "San Francisco's Incredible Expanding Budget." San Francisco Magazine. Modern Luxury, 17 Mar. 2016. Web. 18 May 2017.

36. Knight, Heather. "Budget Projections Show Deficits Rising in S.F." San Francisco Chronicle. N.p., 03 Dec. 2016. Web. 18 May 2017.

37. Mickle, Tripp. "Apple's Cash Hoard Set to Top $250 Billion." The Wall Street Journal. Dow Jones & Company, 30 Apr. 2017. Web. 18 May 2017.

38. Final Apple Campus 2 Project EIR Response to Comments Document: State Clearinghouse No. 2011082055. Berkeley, CA: LSA Associates, 2013. Https://s3.amazonaws.com. Office of Community Development Cuppertino, June 2013. Web. 18 May 2017.

39. Frequently Asked Questions : City of Cupertino General Plan Amendment. City of Cupertino, 1 Dec. 2014. Web. 18 May 2017.

40. "Apple Park Opens to Employees in April." Apple Newsroom. N.p., 22 Feb. 2017. Web. 18 May 2017.

41. Ovide, Shira, and Rani Molla. "Technology Conquers Stock Market." Bloomberg.com. Bloomberg, 02 Aug. 2016. Web. 18 May 2017.

42. O'Malley, Marianne. "Understanding Proposition 218." Legislative Analyst's Office, Dec. 1996. Web. 18 May 2017.

43. "The Trouble with Tax Reform." The Economist. The Economist Newspaper, 04 Feb. 2011. Web. 18 May 2017.

44. "US companies braced for tax shake-up as Apple feud escalates." Financial Times. The Financial Times Limited, 05 Aug. 2016.

45. "California's Fiscal Outlook." The 2017-18 Budget: California's Fiscal Outlook. Legislative Analysts' Office, 16 Nov. 2016. Web. 18 May 2017.

46. Garosi, Justin, and Jason Sisney. ""Top 1 Percent" Pays Half of State Income Taxes." California Economy and Taxes. Legislative Analysts' Office, 4 Dec. 2014. Web. 18 May 2017.

47. "California's Fiscal Outlook." The 2017-18 Budget: California's Fiscal Outlook. Legislative Analysts' Office, 16 Nov. 2016. Web. 18 May 2017.

48. Cutler, Joyce E. "San Francisco Income Tax Resolution Moves Ahead." San Francisco Income Tax Resolution Moves Ahead | Bloomberg BNA. Bloomberg BNA, 17 Mar. 2017. Web. 18 May 2017.

49. "Stop Dreamin'." The Economist. The Economist Newspaper, 09 July 2016. Web. 18 May 2017.

50. Myers, John. "California's Budget Rainy-day Fund Is Expected to Grow to Almost $8 Billion." Los Angeles Times. Los Angeles Times, 10 Jan. 2017. Web. 18 May 2017.

51. Auerbach, Alan J. "Californiaís Future Tax System." University of California, Berkeley (n.d.): n. University of California, Berkeley, 5 Apr. 2010. Web. 18 Mar. 2017.

52. State of California Office of the Controller. "Comprehensive Tax Reform in California: A Contextual Framework." California State Controller Betty T. Yee & the Controller's Council of Economic Advisors on Tax Reform, June 2016. Web. 18 May 2017.

53. Culwell, Alexa Cortés, and Heather Mcleod Grant. "The Giving Code: Silicon Valley Nonprofits and Philanthropy." (2016): Open Impact. Web. 18 May 2017.

54. Ibid.

55. Ibid.

56. Karlinsky, Sarah, and Kristy Wang. Non-Primary Residences and San Francisco's Housing Market. Rep. SPUR, 21 Oct. 2014. Web. 18 May 2017.

57. Nguyen, My. "Local Realtors Reign in National Rankings." Palo Alto Online. N.p., 06 July 2015. Web. 18 May 2017.

58. Swartz, Angela. "Who's Buying Now?" Palo Alto Online. N.p., 17 Feb. 2017. Web. 18 May 2017.

59. Sa, Filipa. "The Effect of Foreign Investors on Local Housing Markets: Evidence from the UK." VOX CEPR's Policy Portal Research-based Policy Analysis and Commentary from Leading Economists. N.p., 4 Jan. 2017. Web. 18 May 2017.

60. Kassam, Ashifa. "Vancouver Slaps 15% Tax on Foreign House Buyers in Effort to Cool Market." The Guardian. Guardian News and Media, 02 Aug. 2016. Web. 18 May 2017.

61. Gauder, Maurice, Claire Houssard, and David Orsmond. "Foreign Investment in Residential Real Estate." (n.d.): Reserve Bank of Australia, June 2014. Web. 18 May 2017.

62. Story, Louise. "U.S. Will Track Secret Buyers of Luxury Real Estate." The New York Times. The New York Times, 13 Jan. 2016. Web. 18 May 2017.

63. Karlinsky, Sarah, and Kristy Wang. Non-Primary Residences and San Francisco's Housing Market. Rep. SPUR, 21 Oct. 2014. Web. 18 May 2017.

64. Terrazas on 4/28/2017, Aaron. "Are Home Buyers From China Competing With Americans?" Zillow Research. N.p., 28 Apr. 2017. Web. 18 May 2017.

LET'S BUILD
HOUSING FOR ALL

JOIN A LOCAL YIMBY GROUP TODAY

UNITED STATES OF AMERICA

CALIFORNIA

California Renters Legal Advocacy and Education Fund carlaef.org
California YIMBY cayimby.org
YIMBY Action yimbyaction.org

San Francisco Bay Area

Balanced Mountain View balancedmv.org
East Bay for Everyone eastbayforeveryone.org
Greenbelt Alliance greenbelt.org
Grow the Richmond growtherichmond.com
Imagine Menlo imaginemenlo.com
Livable Berkeley livableberkeley.org
Livermore Rising livermorerising.com
Mission YIMBY facebook.com/missionyimby
Palo Alto Forward paloaltoforward.com
Progress Noe Valley progressnoe.com
Redwood City Forward redwoodcityforward.com
SF Bay Area Renters Federation sfbarf.org

San Francisco Bay Area (continued)

SF Housing Action Coalition sfhac.org
SF YIMBY sfyimby.org
South Bay YIMBY southbayyimby.org
SPUR spur.org
Tech for Housing techforhousing.org
The New SOMA Neighborhood Coalition facebook.com/NewSOMASF

Central Coast

Santa Cruz YIMBY @SantaCruzYIMBY

Los Angeles

Abundant Housing LA abundanthousingla.org
LA Yimby layimby.org
LAplus la-plus.org

Orange County

People for Housing OC peopleforhousing.org

Sacramento

House Sacramento housesac.org

San Diego

Housing You Matters housingyoumatters.org

COLORADO

Better Boulder betterboulder.com
YIMBY Denver yimbydenver.com

MASSACHUSETTS

A Better Cambridge abettercambridge.org
Engine 6 enginesix.org
JP YIMBY @JPYIMBY
Somerville YIMBY somervilleyimby.org
The Massachusetts Smart Growth Alliance ma-smartgrowth.org
WalkUP Roslindale walkuproslindale.org

MINNESOTA

MSPyimby mspyimby.com

NEW JERSEY

Walkable Princeton walkableprinceton.com

NEW YORK

More New York morenewyork.org

OREGON

Bend YIMBY bendyimby.com
Portlanders for Parking Reform pdxshoupistas.com

TEXAS

AURA aura-atx.org
Evolve Austin evolveaustin.org

WASHINGTON

#YIOBY @YIMBYsea
Seattle Tech 4 Housing seattletech4housing.org
Sightline Institute sightline.org
The Urbanist theurbanist.org

WASHINGTON, D.C.

Greater Greater Washington ggwash.org

INTERNATIONAL

Urbz urbz.net
YIMBY Wiki yimby.wiki

AUSTRALIA

YIMBY Qld yimbyqld.com.au
YIMBY Sydney @YIMBYSydney

CANADA

All In allinadvocacy.ca

Ontario

Future Kingston futurekingston.com
Housing Matters torontohousingmatters.com
YIMBY Toronto yimbytoronto.org

Vancouver

Abundant Housing YVR abundanthousingvancouver.com
CityStudio Vancouver citystudiovancouver.com

ITALY

YIMBY Italy yimbyitaly.it

SWEDEN

YIMBY Göteborg gbg.yimby.se
YIMBY Stockholm yimby.se
YIMBY Uppsala uppsala.yimby.se
YIMBY Malmö malmo.yimby.se

UNITED KINGDOM

Abundant Housing London @AbundantHomeLDN
London YIMBY londonyimby.org

For updates and further details, visit yimbyaction.org/directory.
Don't see a YIMBY group in your area? Start one!
YIMBY Action will help you. Email hello@yimbyaction.org.

THANKS TO OUR MANY DONORS

This book was made possible by more than 150 Kickstarter backers, including the following YIMBYs who gave particularly generous contributions.

Jaina Bee
Trevor Blackwell
Laura & Dan Fingal-Surma

Jeff Andrade-Fong
Tim Bauman
Alexia & Niko Bonatsos
Cole Brennan
Gagan Biyani
Darrin Brown
Daniel Camp
Austin Chang
Travis Cole
Wei Deng
Nicolas Dessaigne
Donald Dewsnup
Jon Dishotsky
Fred Ehrsam
Michael Eyal
Zach Franklin
Brett Gladstone
Adam Gutterman
David Hua
Daniel Kan
Andrew Lee
Libby Lee-Egan
Josh Warren Lehner
Kat Manalac

Mark Mollineaux
Jeremy Stoppelman
Garry Tan

Claire McDonnell
Michael Nielsen
Alexis Ohanian
Ethan Phelps-Goodman
Sam Phillips
Francis Quinn
John Ripley
Scott Simmons
Lars Skjerping
John Stockdale
Kenny Stone
Jason Tan
Calvin Tonini
Aaron VanDevender
Mike Vernal
Robby Walker
Jaap Weel
Matt Werner
Richard White
Vincent Woo
Cameron Yarbrough
Oliver Zhu
Ben Zotto